# ABOUT
# EARTHQUAKES

# ABOUT EARTHQUAKES

BY G. A. EIBY, M.SC., F.R.A.S.
*Geophysicist at the Seismological Observatory*
*Wellington, New Zealand*

*Illustrated*

HARPER & ROW · PUBLISHERS

*New York and Evanston*

ABOUT EARTHQUAKES
*Copyright © 1957 By G. A. Eiby*
*Printed in the United States of America*

This book is published in England
under the title of EARTHQUAKES

*Library of Congress catalog card number: 57-6137*

GLENDOWER:
The frame and huge foundation of the earth
Shak'd like a coward. . . .
I say the earth did shake when I was born. . . .
The heavens were all on fire, the earth did tremble . . . .

HOTSPUR:
Diseased Nature oftentimes breaks forth
In strange eruptions: oft the teeming earth
Is with a kind of colic pinch'd and vex'd
By the imprisoning of unruly wind
Within her womb; which, for enlargement striving,
Shakes the old beldam earth, and topples down
Steeples, and moss-grown towers. At your birth
Our granddam earth, having this distemperature,
In passion shook.

SHAKESPEARE: **Henry IV, Pt. 1**

# Acknowledgements

IN addition to those mentioned in the Preface, the author would like to record his indebtedness and thanks to the following people and organisations for help of various kinds:

To Mr. R. C. Hayes, Superintendent of the Seismological Observatory, Wellington, for all seismograms reproduced, and for Figure 50 and Plate II.

To Mr. R. W. Willett, Director of the Geological Survey of the Department of Scientific and Industrial Research for permission to reproduce Plates XI, XVIII, XXII, and XXIII; and to Mr. Lensen of his staff for help in locating pictures.

To Mr. C. R. H. Taylor, Librarian of the Alexander Turnbull Library, Wellington, for Plates XIV, XIX, XX, XXI, XXIV, XXV, XXVI, XXVII, XXVIII, XXIX, XXX, and XXI, and for Figure 54.

To Mr. N. Modriniak, Superintendent, N.Z. Geophysical Survey, for the reflection survey record in Figure 26.

To Dr. E. Silgado F., Chief of the Seismological Service of the Instituto Geofisico del Peru, for Plates XV and XVI.

To Prof. A. Heim, of Zurich, Switzerland, for Plate XIII.

To the Geotechnical Corporation, Houston, Texas, U.S.A., for Plates IV and VI.

To Hilger and Watts Ltd., London, England, for Plate III.

To the Cambridge Scientific Instrument Co., Cambridge, England, for Plate XXXII.

To the Photographic Section, Information Bureau, N.Z. Department of Scientific and Industrial Research, for Plates VII, VIII, IX, and X; and especially to Messrs. E. Thornley and N. S. Beatus of the Section for help in preparing Plate I, and for copying seismograms and other material.

7

## ACKNOWLEDGEMENTS

To Prof. Beno Gutenberg, Prof. C. F. Richter, and to the Princeton University Press, for Figures 46 and 47, which have been taken from Gutenberg and Richter's *Seismicity of the Earth*.

To the publishers of *Life* magazine for permission to reproduce Plate XVII.

All other photographs and figures are the work of the author.

G. A. EIBY

*July* 1956

# Contents

The Size of the Earth
The Geological Column
The Modified Mercalli Scale
Distances in Miles, Kilometres and Degrees
Historical Earthquakes, 1500–1904
Important Earthquakes since 1904
Major Earthquakes in New Zealand
A Short Book List

# List of Plates

## LIST OF PLATES

# List of Figures

## LIST OF FIGURES

# *Preface*

EARTHQUAKE study is neither a dreary compilation of ancient tales of desolation and destruction nor an attempt at the exploitation of human misfortunes for journalistic sensation. Seismologists are at work in every civilised country, and in many that are not, from the deserts of the tropics to the icy mountains of the Antarctic. No other part of the globe is so inaccessible as that lying directly beneath our feet, but by studying earthquake records the scientist is able to penetrate to the centre, revealing new and valuable deposits of oil and minerals on the way. Yet this is not all of seismology. In countries where earthquakes are frequent, the scientific aspects are matched by social and economic ones of great importance, and special problems confront the architect and the engineer. Earthquakes are an important part of man's environment, and no part of the globe can claim to be completely immune from them.

It would be unfair to conceal from the reader that this book was first started in order to satisfy local requests for "a book about earthquakes". Many ordinary people come to the observatory where I work for information, and the absence of a suitable book has been obvious to me for some years. Once I started to write, I realised that something more than a parochial account was needed, and *Earthquakes* is the result. It is only natural that I should draw many (but by no means all) of my examples from New Zealand, but the reader will have no difficulty in finding others, and I hope he will be stimulated to do so. The importance of earthquake studies is international, and no apology is needed for offering this book to those who have never felt, and may never feel, the slightest evidence of tectonic upheaval. My subject is what we know of the make-up

15

of our planet, and the methods by which science has gathered this knowledge.

If this book were written for my scientific colleagues, it would contain detailed references to the source of all the facts; and many ifs and buts and reservations about the opinions. In the interest of the general reader, these have been left out, but I hope that it is still possible to distinguish fact from opinion, and evidence from conclusion.

On page 7 specific permission to quote and to reproduce illustrations is listed, but this by no means exhausts my debt to others. If any due acknowledgement has been omitted, I apologise. In any subject, in any age, a few great names stand out: like those of Gutenberg and Richter, Jeffreys and Bullen; but before them Milne and Turner, Galitzin, Wiechert, and Omori; and so back, if you will, through Mallet and Michell to Lucretius and Aristotle. It is inevitable that these men should contribute to a book of this kind; but there is also a contribution from nearer home, from those with whom daily discussions are possible, most of them fellow officers in the Department of Scientific and Industrial Research. Neither they nor the Department, of course, are responsible for the opinions I express.

Special thanks are due to Dr. E. I. Robertson, Director of the Geophysics Division, who first suggested that this book might have an interest beyond New Zealand; and to Mr. R. R. Dibble of the Seismological Observatory staff, who has read the manuscript critically. Above all, I must place on record my debt to the man who gave me my first practical training as a seismologist, Mr. R. C. Hayes, first Acting Director, and later Director and Superintendent of the Seismological Observatory, Wellington. From these men, and from many more, I have learned. For the inadequacies of what is to follow, the pupil alone is responsible.

G. A. EIBY

*Khandallah*
*May* 1955

# By Way of Introduction

THIRD AVOCATORE: I've an earthquake in me!
BEN JONSON: *Volpone*

EARTHQUAKES were among the earliest discoveries to be made in New Zealand. Members of Captain Cook's expeditions felt them in the eighteenth century, and within ten years of the foundation of Wellington, the colonists lost their chimneys. In about a hundred and fifty years, eighty shocks strong enough to cause major damage to buildings have been reported. Fortunately there has been little loss of life. Less than three hundred people have been killed in New Zealand earthquakes, and the Hawkes Bay earthquake of 1931 accounted for two hundred and sixty of these. The New Zealander is much more likely to die in a road accident than in an earthquake; but damage to property has cost him a great deal. Almost two million pounds were spent in repairing the damage caused by the Masterton earthquakes of 1942, and the present cost of replacing a city like Napier would hardly be less than ten or twenty million. The study of earthquakes, therefore, has a special claim to be regarded as the New Zealander's own science. Earthquakes are a major problem, economic, social, and scientific. It is therefore hardly surprising that the seismologist finds his friends encouraging him to "talk shop".

Observatories, perhaps to a greater degree than other scientific institutions, tend to attract visitors; but many of them find the seismologist's headquarters a disappointment. In a cellar beneath the building about half a dozen instruments each produce a daily chart with wiggly lines on it. The charts are made photographically, so that the whole arrangement has to be kept in a dim red light, and it is not possible to see anything

17

happening. In the offices above, members of the staff spend their time putting more marks on the charts, and making entries in ledgers. Few visitors consider this a fitting manner in which to treat so momentous an affair as an earthquake. A talk with the staff is needed to reveal that they at least find the study of earthquakes full of interest. In the book that follows, I will try to answer the kind of question that our visitors generally ask, and to give an idea of what the instruments look like with the covers off. By far the largest number of people who have dealings with the observatory are ordinary citizens who report the times and intensities of all the shocks they feel. This is a most valuable service; and these reporters, most of whom lack technical training, should find this an understandable account of what happens to their observations.

Seismology forms part of the larger science called Geophysics, which overlaps and bridges the gap between the older sciences of Geology and Physics. In its widest sense, geology is concerned with the complete study of the earth, but it is more usually limited to a largely descriptive study of the nature of rocks, where they occur, and how they are transformed at the hand of Nature. Physics considers the behaviour of all forms of matter under the influence of heat, pressure, electricity, and other forces. Geophysics has therefore come into being to deal with those parts of geology which involve precise measurement and calculation, and with those parts of physics which concern the earth and its atmosphere.

Scientific seismology is amongst the youngest of the sciences. It is less than three-quarters of a century since the first satisfactory recordings of ground movement were made, and only half a century since the beginnings of a world network of earthquake recording stations. Even today there are gaps in this network; and there are only two or three regions where stations are close enough together to enable detailed study of the smaller shocks. Seismology has the whole earth as its field, and is necessarily international; but wherever possible I will try to use New Zealand illustrations of the effects described. Whilst this should increase its interest to my fellow countrymen, I do not think it will detract from its interest and use to others, and it will make material available which would otherwise be difficult to obtain. New Zealand earthquake study in many respects offers more complex problems than those experienced in other seismic regions; and closer study often results only in revealing further complexities. Nevertheless, we now understand something of the nature and causes of earthquakes, and of the manner in which buildings will behave when shaken. I have tried to distinguish opinion from fact throughout the book, but it is the nature of any living science to change and develop. To omit all reference to those parts of the subject where the experts differ is to deprive the reader of the opportunity to see the problems which attract the scientist.

There is no special merit in the order of chapters. They appear in the way they "came out". The reader whose interest lies more in geology than physics, or more in building construction than in the interior of the earth may chose to read them in a different order. If terms are encountered which have not been explained, reference to the index should clear the matter up.

# CHAPTER ONE

## On Feeling an Earthquake

DON PEDRO: . . . Thou wilt quake for this shortly.
BENEDICK: I look for an earthquake then.
SHAKESPEARE: *Much Ado About Nothing*

FROM time to time, the surface of the earth undergoes a sudden and more or less violent shaking. At its mildest it may be taken for the passing of a heavy truck, or for a gust of wind; but at its most severe it can destroy buildings, roads, and bridges, move hillsides, and give rise to huge waves which sweep inland from the coast and complete the destruction which the shaking began.

Man's first reaction was a superstitious awe. In the seventeenth century, a New England preacher could still declare that such events were a clear evidence of "the chastening rod of God". Proof of this, he asserted, could be found in the fact that the disturbances were directed only at cities, and not towards "desarts and uninhabited places". Since no records were forthcoming from the uninhabited places, his thesis went unchallenged.

If we are to discover *how* earthquakes originate, we must first determine *where* they originate, and this involves systematic observation. One of the simplest ways in which this can be undertaken is to visit the affected region, and to map the region of maximum damage. As we shall see, evidence of this nature needs careful interpretation if false conclusions are to be avoided. The first extensive study of this kind appeared in 1862, when Robert Mallet, an Irish engineer, published two beautifully illustrated volumes with the title *The Great Neapolitan Earthquake of 1857; the first Principles of Observational Seismology*. Mallet drew a map of the affected region, which he divided into four zones. In the first, whole towns were destroyed; in the second, large buildings were thrown down and people killed; in the third there was only minor damage and no casualties; and in the fourth, although the shock was felt, no damage was reported.

This method was very useful for large earthquakes, but the true centre of the disturbance could not be located with very great accuracy. Clearly, instruments were called for; and the history of earthquake study for the next half-century is very largely the story of the search for a suitable recorder, and the interpretation of the records it made. In spite of the development of recording instruments, the felt earthquake scale has retained its importance, and in countries where shocks are common, the general public has at least heard of the scales of Rossi and Forel, and of the modified Mercalli scale, which is the one in general use in New Zealand today.

The felt reporting system in New Zealand is organised by the Seismological Observatory of the Department of Scientific and Industrial Research, in Wellington, and covers the whole country with a network of voluntary observers. These include postal officials, lighthouse keepers, cinema managers, and private citizens. Whenever an observer feels an earthquake, he fills in a simple form, and forwards it to the observatory for correlation with other reports. The form asks for the date and time of the shock, an estimate of its duration and the direction of movement, information about sounds heard, and the strength on the modified Mercalli scale. It is this last information which is generally of the most value. Times are generally poorly estimated. Few people have an accurate idea of the length of a second, so that the early American report from a Jesuit missionary who described an earthquake as lasting "as long as a *Paternoster* or a little longer" must be regarded as exceptionally accurate.

The Mercalli scale, given in full in the Appendix, is probably the best suited to New Zealand conditions, and unlike many of the earlier scales, can be used for shocks having a great range of intensity. It extends from I, which is a barely perceptible shock, to XII, which represents a truly awesome state of destruction, and lists the effects in homely terms which untrained observers have little difficulty in distinguishing from one another. It is always necessary to translate a scale of this kind into local terms. The observatory in Australia which gives as one of the degrees on its scale "like a horse rubbing itself against the verandah post" would have little use for the description "sets church bells ringing" which is common in the scales used on the continent of Europe. As an example of the completely misleading, I might quote a scale beginning "felt only by an experienced observer".

When the observatory has collected the reports of a shock, the intensities are plotted on a map of the district involved (usually about half the country), and lines are drawn in such a way as to enclose the areas of the same intensity. These lines are known as "isoseismals". Figure 1 shows a map of this kind

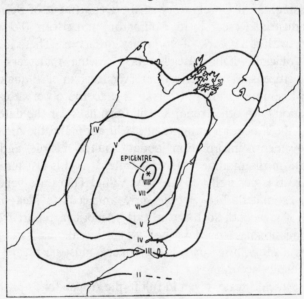

FIG. 1. ISOSEISMAL MAP
Distribution of felt intensity in the Waiau earthquake in May 1948. Strengths are given on the modified Mercalli scale.

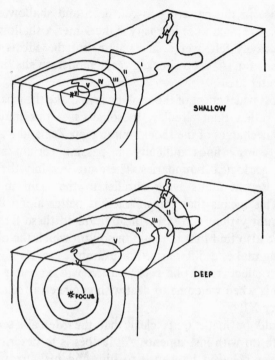

SHALLOW

DEEP

*FOCUS

FIG. 2

Isoseismal patterns for deep and shallow earthquakes with the same epicentre and the same maximum felt intensity.

for the Waiau earthquake in May 1948. As a rule, the origin of the shock will lie beneath the centre of the highest isoseismal; but there are often some peculiar departures from the rule, either on account of irregularities in the geological structure of the country, or on account of the depth at which the shock originated.

If the earth was of exactly the same constitution in all places, we could expect the energy to spread out evenly in all directions from the origin of the earthquake (a region known as the "focus") so that the most severely shaken spot would be at the "epicentre", the point on the surface directly above the focus; and the intensity would fall off gradually and evenly as we went away from it. Figure 2 shows one reason why there is

23

a difference in the pattern between deep and shallow shocks, even when the maximum intensity is the same. A shallow shock may be heavily felt over a small area, but the effects do not extend very far. A deep shock gives a moderate shaking to a much greater area.

The most usual effect of the geology is to make the isoseismals elliptical rather than circular. In some cases this may result from the mechanics of the shock, but in New Zealand it appears that the energy finds difficulty in passing certain strongly reflecting geological boundaries. These are possibly the planes of large Recent faults lying parallel to the main mountain ranges. This means that transmission is better along the axis of the country than across it. In addition to these large-scale effects, we also find that the kind of soil on which the observer is standing makes a difference. For example, gravels give quite a different effect from solid rock; but we will be better able to discuss this when we come to deal with engineering seismology in Chapter XI.

It should be made quite clear that the Mercalli scale has nothing to do with instruments. All it does is to describe what an observer believed happened to him and his surroundings. Every earthquake has therefore a great number of intensities, depending on where you happened to be at the time. If you didn't feel it at all, then as far as you are concerned, the intensity was zero.

Earthquakes can be felt on ships at sea, as well as on dry land, but the effect is rather different. As a rule, there is just a single upward jolt, as if the ship had struck a submerged obstacle. This is a result of the fact that liquids can only transmit some of the waves that can travel through the solid earth, and these waves are bent sharply upwards as they leave the earth for the water at the ocean bottom. These different wave types will be discussed later. Seismic sea waves, which are discussed in Chapter X, are not usually noticeable on the high seas, but in coastal waters or in harbours the effects can be serious.

There can be few phenomena which have not at one time or another been considered to have some connection with earthquakes. Birds and fish have both been credited with some form of prescience, and the behaviour of zoo animals before, during and after earthquakes has been recorded in detail. Connections between earthquakes and the weather are popular with the public, sometimes with the earthquakes as the cause of the weather, and sometimes the other way round. Nearly all of the ideas in the first class are wrong, but there is some evidence that certain weather conditions may "trigger" an earthquake. We will return to this later. The popular conception of "earthquake weather" has no foundation in fact.

Among the effects which most commonly accompany an earthquake are a variety of noises. They can usually be classified either as explosions, or as rumbles. In the case of the rumbles, it is generally difficult to separate the true earthquake noises from the protests of the building in which the observer is situated; but since they are also reported out of doors, there is no doubt of their reality. The sound is very low in pitch, and lies in the part of the musical scale where hearing and feeling become almost the same thing. Very often, it is described as preceding the earthquake, but this probably means that it accompanied the compressional wave (see Chapter III), which was too small to be felt. The explosions are generally of the nature of a low boom, and may indicate that the shock originated in a different way from the ones which produce a rumble; but the data are generally too imprecise to allow an interpretation. The distribution of the places at which the sound is heard often shows an irregular pattern. This results at least in part from the atmospheric conditions at the time, rather than in anything connected with the earthquake itself.

The appearance of lights and glows in the sky has occasionally been reported. This seems very doubtful. Most of those which could be checked have turned out to have no connection with the shock. Meteor showers, lightning, and faults in electric power lines have all been mistaken for earthquake effects.

In some very large earthquakes, reliable observers have described the appearance of waves on the surface of the ground. One report of this kind tells of waves travelling rapidly across the concrete floor of a garage, about a foot in height, and two or three times this from crest to crest. Since the size of the waves involved in an earthquake does not tally in any respect with this description, and since any concrete subjected to such a movement would undoubtedly be shattered, the suggestion that such a thing actually occurred must be ruled out. However, something of the kind has so often been reported in good faith that it must be supposed that violent shaking so affects a man as to produce an illusion of this kind. With this demonstration of human fallibility it is as well to pass to the problem of instrumental recording.

# CHAPTER TWO

# Recording an Earthquake

The moving finger writes; and having writ
Moves on:
FITZGERALD: *Rubaiyat of Omar Khayyam*

RECORDING the motion of the ground during an earthquake is not an easy matter. The difficulty when every-
thing fixed to the earth is moving with it is to obtain some
stationary point to start from. The method the seismologist
adopts is to make use of "inertia", the tendency a heavy body
has to "stay put". A weight hanging from a flexible support
tends to lag behind when the support is moved. When some
method of recording the relative movement of the weight and
the support is provided, we have a primitive form of seismograph. The main defect of the arrangement is that once the
support is moved, the weight will eventually follow; and it
will tend to go on swinging after the support has come to rest.
Quite a simple movement of the support becomes a most
complicated movement of the weight, and it needs skill and
experience to say exactly what the record indicates. When
complicated movements are given to the support, it becomes
almost impossible.

Science progresses by a combination of theory and experiment, and it will be easier to understand how the seismograph
works if we perform a simple experiment ourselves. Get a piece
of string about three feet long, and tie a small but reasonably
heavy weight to one end. Hold on to the other end, and lift
the weight just clear of the floor. Move your hand very slowly
backwards and forwards. The weight will follow without any
tendency to swing, so that there is no relative movement between the hand and the weight. If you increase the speed of the

27

to-and-fro movement, the weight will begin to swing more and more vigorously. When you change the direction of movement of your hand about once a second, the swings of the weight will get very big, even if the movements of your hand are quite small. This occurs when the natural period of swing of the pendulum and the period of movement of your hand are the same. Under these conditions, you are obviously getting a big magnification of the movement of your hand, but when you stop, the pendulum will go on swinging, and give a spurious record. Stop the weight, and then try a sudden rapid to-and-fro movement of your hand. The weight remains almost stationary, whilst your hand moves relative to it. In this case we have just about reached the condition we need for recording the movement of the support in an earthquake. There are two disadvantages. There is very little magnification; and if we are going to measure the slower earthquake waves, we will need a pendulum which has a very long time of swing. Plate I shows photographs of an experiment of this kind, but the wise reader will repeat it for himself.

If we sum up the results of our experiment with a simple pendulum, we can see how to apply the knowledge to the design of a simple practical seismograph.

1. When the period of movement of the support is much longer than the natural period of the pendulum, the weight just follows the support, and the magnification is zero.

2. When the period of the support movement is the same as the natural period of the pendulum, the magnification is very large.

3. When the period of the support movement is short compared with the natural period of the pendulum, the magnification is nearly one.

These results can be shown even more clearly in the form of a graph (Figure 3).

We can obtain a very faithful record of the ground motion if the period of the instrument is long compared with that of the movement; or a very high magnification if the periods are nearly the same. If we provide some drag on the pendulum which will bring it to rest as soon as possible after the disturbance has stopped, it becomes easier to reach a useful compromise. The drag is called "damping", and can be arranged by fixing a small vane to the pendulum, which either creates

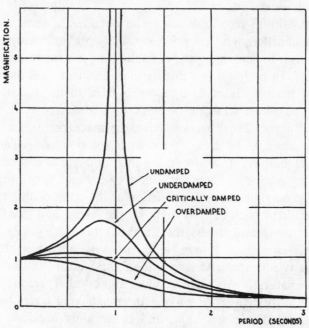

FIG. 3. MAGNIFICATION OF A SEISMOGRAPH

Seismograph with a natural period of one second and different values of damping, when recording ground movements of different period.

air resistance, or trails in a bath of oil. In more elaborate instruments, the vane is made of copper or aluminium, and moves between the poles of a strong magnet. The eddy currents which are generated when it moves will have the same damping effect, and cannot be upset by changes in temperature, air pressure, or humidity. The amount of damping is often arranged to be "critical", that is to say, when the pendulum has been displaced, it will just return to the zero position without additional swings. The figure shows how the magnification is affected by altering the amount of damping. A critically damped pendulum gives a fairly faithful picture of the ground movement over quite a wide range of periods, and by choosing the proper damping and pendulum period, it is possible to design a seismograph suitable for studying most of the problems in which we are interested.

Since faithful recording has to be obtained at the expense of magnification, a seismograph is usually provided with some mechanism for enlarging the pendulum movement before it is recorded. In early instruments, levers were used, and the permanent record was made by a stylus fixed to the end of the last lever, which scratched a mark on a drum covered with smoked paper. These records could be made permanent and clean to handle by fixing them in a solution of shellac in methylated spirit. Instruments of this kind are still used for recording strong earthquakes, but they are not very suitable for large magnifications. The friction at the point of the stylus is transmitted back to the weight by the levers, and interferes with its movement unless the weight is made very large. In Europe, seismographs were built with suspended weights as large as twenty tons. At least one of these is still in use, but they are naturally expensive to house and instal. There are also mechanical difficulties in making the magnifying levers themselves both strong and light, and in avoiding backlash and "lost motion" at the pivots.

Most present-day instruments use photographic recording, either directly or indirectly. The direct method is to fix a small mirror to the pendulum, and to reflect a beam of light from it on to a sheet of light-sensitive paper wrapped about a recording drum. Every schoolboy who has played with a piece of mirror on a sunny day will know that a very small movement of the mirror produces a very large movement of the reflected light spot. In this way, the pendulum movement can be magnified and recorded without introducing any friction or interference from the levers. When the paper is developed, the movements

Plate III

MILNE-SHAW HORIZON-
TAL PENDULUM SEIS-
MOGRAPH. The wooden
draught cover has been removed, and the recording
drum is out of the picture to
the left. Beneath the boom at
the left hand end, and partly
obscured by it, is the small
circular recording mirror,
which hangs from a pivot on
the small rectangular stand,
and is connected to the boom
by the light L-shaped aluminium coupling. The large mirror fixed to the right hand
levelling screw is used in calibrating the instrument.

Plate IV
BENIOFF VARIABLE RE-
LUCTANCE SEISMOMETER.
This plate shows the vertical com-
ponent instrument which is shown
in cross section in Fig. 6.

of the spot will appear as black lines on a white background.

The indirect method is perhaps the most commonly used
today, although direct types are far from being out of date.
Instruments which use indirect recording are called electromagnetic seismographs. In these the pendulum carries a small
pick-up coil, which can swing between the poles of a magnet
mounted on the frame of the instrument. Whenever it moves,
an electric current is generated, and this is fed to a galvanometer, a sensitive meter with a mirror instead of a pointer.
The movements of the galvanometer mirror are then recorded
on photographic paper just as those of the pendulum were in
the direct method. At first sight, the extra instrument might
seem to be an unnecessary complication, but it has a number
of advantages. Firstly, the part of the instrument which is
sensitive to ground movement can be placed some distance
from the recording drum, and is consequently less likely to be
disturbed by the visits of the operator. Secondly, electric
currents are very simple to control, and they can be amplified,
reduced, or modified in a great number of ways for special
purposes. Electromagnetic seismographs have the further
advantages that they can be operated in daylight, and that they
are unaffected by ground tilt. When mechanical or direct
recording seismographs are used, slow tilting of the ground
causes the zero position of the spot to wander, and the lines
on the chart become unevenly spaced. When the tilting is
severe, the lines overlap and make the record difficult to read.
In an electromagnetic instrument, the size of the current
generated depends upon the speed at which the coil moves,
and not upon the distance it travels, so that these slow movements do not have any appreciable effect. Figure 4 shows some
of the different kinds of pendulums that can be used as seismometers.

Before I describe some actual observatory seismographs, a
more unassuming part of the equipment must be mentioned—
the recording drum. A complete seismograph consists of two

31

equally important parts—the seismometer, which is sensitive to ground movements, and the recorder, which makes its indications permanent. The recorder may seem so simple as to be unworthy of discussion. It consists of a drum, about a foot in diameter and the same in length, with a motor to turn it round, usually either twice or four times in an hour, and a screw arrangement to move it slowly sideways so that the successive traces do not overlap. The slow speed is very difficult

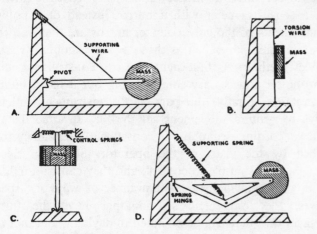

FIG. 4. COMMON TYPES OF SEISMOGRAPH

A. Horizontal Pendulum      B. Torsion Seismograph
C. Inverted Pendulum      D. Vertical Seismograph

Types A and B respond to movements at right angles to the plane of the paper, type C to movements across the paper, and type D to up and down movements. Damping and recording arrangements are not shown.

to keep constant. Small irregularities in the gears are serious, and if the drum is not perfectly balanced it will run ahead at times and then wait for the motor to catch up. Since the seismologist sometimes wants to measure the time of arrival of a wave with an accuracy of a tenth of a second, ordinary clockwork cannot be used for the motor. Clock escapements drive the hands in a series of jerks which may be a fifth or even half a second apart. The steadiest drives for recording drums are synchronous motors, driven by a specially generated

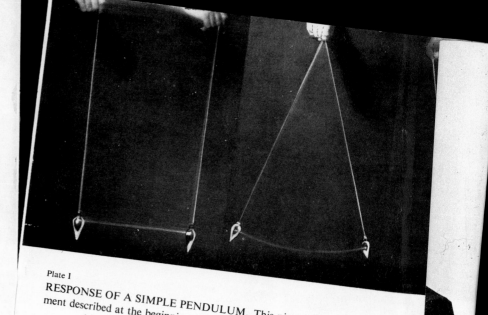

Plate I

RESPONSE OF A SIMPLE PENDULUM. This picture shows the three stages of ment described at the beginning of Chapter II.

(a) Movement slower than natural period.
(b) Movement coincides with natural period.
(c) Movement faster than natural period.

Plate II

WOOD-ANDERSON TORSION SEISMOMETER.

(a) View from the direction of the recorder.
(b) Two short-period suspensions in travelling case. The wires, which h thickened so as to appear in the photograph, are approximately 1/100
(c) Rear view of the seismometer with the cover off and the suspension r

electric current whose frequency is controlled by a tuning fork in a sealed and temperature-controlled enclosure.

Along with the drum goes a recording lamp. Its light is focused upon the seismometer mirror by a series of lenses, and reflected back upon the surface of the drum as a tiny but sharply defined spot. If this spot is not clear and sharp, the timing accuracy will suffer and very fast movements cannot be clearly seen. Somewhere in the path of the light beam there is a shutter which is closed for an instant once a minute by an accurate clock, leaving a brief gap in the trace. In some instruments, instead of a shutter, a glass prism is used, and the trace is moved sideways instead of being blacked out. In this way none of the record is lost, but if the movements of the earthquake are large, the timing marks may be hard to see.

Seismographs with many different times of pendulum swing are needed to record all the things which the seismologist wishes to study. At a first glance, it is sometimes difficult to see the similarity between an actual seismograph and the simple arrangement I have described. The standard instrument used in New Zealand for recording local earthquakes is the Wood-Anderson Torsion Seismometer. The way it works can be seen in Figure 5. The "heavy" weight is a tiny cylinder of copper, only about an inch long, and not as thick as a piece of fencing wire. Since we do not ask it to drive anything, we can make it small and convenient. At the top end of the cylinder, a mirror is fixed, and the whole arrangement is carried on a thin tungsten wire about eight or nine inches long. Just above and below the weight, the wire passes through two small holes, each holding a single drop of castor oil. This stops any tendency the wire might have to vibrate like the string of a violin, so that all the weight can do is to twist back and forth around the wire. On either side of the weight, the poles of a magnet provide eddy-current damping. This magnet is somewhat differently arranged in different models of the instrument, but it can always be moved up and down, and by arranging just the right length of the cylinder to come between the poles the damping

33

can be adjusted to critical. This seismograph has a magnification of nearly three thousand, and a period of just over three-quarters of a second.

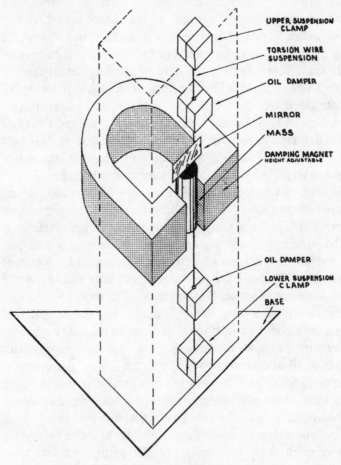

FIG. 5. WOOD-ANDERSON TORSION SEISMOMETER

Some stations use a modified type with a vane instead of a cylinder. These can be run at a much longer period—up to five or six seconds—but the magnification is then only six or seven hundred. Lower magnifications are usual with all long-period

34

instruments. A seismologist generally calls periods of several seconds "long", and those of a second or less "short". Strangely enough, it is the long-period instruments which are used for recording distant earthquakes, although they are made with lower magnifications. This is because of changes which take place in the periods of earthquake waves which travel long distances.

The limit to the magnification which we can use at any particular period is set by small movements of the ground which are called microseisms. They go on all the time, even when there are no earthquakes, and once a seismograph is sensitive enough to show them, an increase in the magnification only makes the recording more and more confused. The most common types of microseism have periods between two and six seconds, so that the long-period instruments are most seriously affected.

A popular long-period seismograph is the Milne Shaw, a direct recording photographic instrument with a period of twelve seconds and a magnification of two hundred and fifty. The pendulum of the Milne Shaw swings on an upper and a lower pivot, rather like a gate, and the movement is magnified by very small and light aluminium levers before being communicated to the mirror (Plate III). It may already have occurred to some readers that although an instrument like this will respond readily to earth movements in one direction, it will be unaffected by movements in a direction at right angles to this, along the line joining the centre of the suspended weight to the hinges. This is quite true, and the well-equipped observatory always has a pair of instruments mounted at right angles; usually, but not always, north and south for one, and east and west for the other. To complete the picture of the ground movement, we need a third instrument, sensitive to up-and-down movements. This has proved to be the most difficult type to construct, but, if we can afford only one instrument, it is probably the most useful to have.

In the vertical seismograph, the only way we can make the

weight free to move up and down is to support it with a spring. This introduces a great many practical difficulties. The spring changes in length and in its elasticity when the temperature changes, and the metal gradually "creeps" as it becomes fatigued. We will take the Galitzin as our example of a vertical instrument, and it will also serve to illustrate the electromagnetic type (Plate V). The weight is fixed to the boom, pivoted on flat springs at the left-hand end, and kept horizontal by the large vertical coiled spring. The pick-up coil and the large copper vane to provide damping are mounted at the other end. By altering the position of the magnets, the amount of current generated in the coil can be varied, so that the magnification can be adjusted to any desired value, generally between three and four hundred. Galitzin seismographs are often made with very long periods—ten seconds or more for the vertical instrument, and as much as double this for the horizontals. There is a set of these instruments at the Christchurch station with twelve- and twenty-four-second periods respectively.

This by no means exhausts the common types of seismograph. The instruments developed by Dr. Benioff in California use a single seismometer to drive galvanometers of different period, and make available some enormous magnifications in the short-period range (Figure 6, Plates IV, VI). In localities free from artificial disturbance and with a low microseism background, they have been operated with magnifications as high as three hundred thousand. The New Zealand Government is installing a set of these instruments at the Apia Observatory in Samoa, and will be sending another set to its Antarctic base in the Ross Sea Dependency for the International Geophysical Year. In New Zealand itself, increasing use is being made of the Willmore, an English instrument with similar characteristics to the Benioff. It suffers somewhat from insufficient damping, and operates only at short periods; but it has the great advantage of being portable and relatively inexpensive, so that it can be used for temporary installations and for site testing.

Now that we have devised a set of instruments that will record the movement of the ground, the next step is to discuss what these records can tell us.

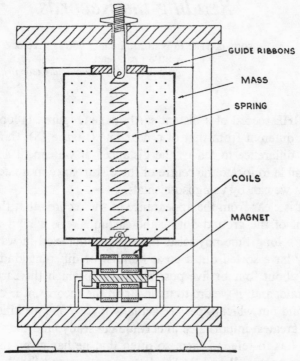

FIG. 6. BENIOFF VERTICAL SEISMOMETER

In this seismometer, the magnet is fixed to the frame of the instrument. The moving pickup coils are carried by the cylindrical mass, which is supported by a spring passing through a central hole.

# Reading the Records

THE record of a distant earthquake (Figure 21) looks quite different from that of a near one (Figure 18). Can we use this difference to tell us the distance? If we can, it should be possible to locate the centre of the disturbance more accurately than we can by using isoseismals.

It is clear from the appearance of the records that the movement of the ground during the earthquake is a kind of wave. For a long time physicists have been interested in waves, and they have sorted out a great number of different kinds. There are about four or five possible ways in which the earth could vibrate, and, if we are to understand the records, it is necessary to find out which types are actually involved. Two kinds are of the greatest importance in earthquake study, and the seismologist has to refer to them so often that he has given them one-letter names, P and S. The letters really stand for "primary" and "secondary" in order of arrival; but it is easier to remember which is which if you think of them as "push" and "shake". The physicist, who likes his names to give a mathematically exact description of what is happening, calls them "longitudinal" and "transverse" or "compressional" and "shear" respectively.

A longitudinal, or P wave, is really a sound wave through the earth, and is the fastest kind. As the wave passes, each particle of the rock moves to and fro in the same direction as the wave is travelling. The material therefore experiences a series of compressions and rarefactions. This is not the simplest of the spot will appear as black lines on a white background.

The indirect method is perhaps the most commonly used today, although direct types are far from being out of date. Instruments which use indirect recording are called electromagnetic seismographs. In these the pendulum carries a small pick-up coil, which can swing between the poles of a magnet mounted on the frame of the instrument. Whenever it moves, an electric current is generated, and this is fed to a galvanometer, a sensitive meter with a mirror instead of a pointer. The movements of the galvanometer mirror are then recorded on photographic paper just as those of the pendulum were in the direct method. At first sight, the extra instrument might seem to be an unnecessary complication, but it has a number of advantages. Firstly, the part of the instrument which is sensitive to ground movement can be placed some distance from the recording drum, and is consequently less likely to be disturbed by the visits of the operator. Secondly, electric currents are very simple to control, and they can be amplified, reduced, or modified in a great number of ways for special purposes. Electromagnetic seismographs have the further advantages that they can be operated in daylight, and that they are unaffected by ground tilt. When mechanical or direct recording seismographs are used, slow tilting of the ground causes the zero position of the spot to wander, and the lines on the chart become unevenly spaced. When the tilting is severe, the lines overlap and make the record difficult to read. In an electromagnetic instrument, the size of the current generated depends upon the speed at which the coil moves, and not upon the distance it travels, so that these slow movements do not have any appreciable effect. Figure 4 shows some of the different kinds of pendulums that can be used as seismometers.

Before I describe some actual observatory seismographs, a more unassuming part of the equipment must be mentioned— the recording drum. A complete seismograph consists of two equally important parts—the seismometer, which is sensitive to ground movements, and the recorder, which makes its indications permanent. The recorder may seem so simple as to be unworthy of discussion. It consists of a drum, about a foot in diameter and the same in length, with a motor to turn it round, usually either twice or four times in an hour, and a screw arrangement to move it slowly sideways so that the successive traces do not overlap. The slow speed is very difficult

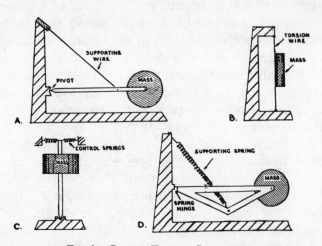

FIG. 4. COMMON TYPES OF SEISMOGRAPH

A. Horizontal Pendulum        B. Torsion Seismograph
C. Inverted Pendulum          D. Vertical Seismograph

Types A and B respond to movements at right angles to the plane of the paper, type C to movements across the paper, and type D to up and down movements. Damping and recording arrangements are not shown.

to keep constant. Small irregularities in the gears are serious, and if the drum is not perfectly balanced it will run ahead at times and then wait for the motor to catch up. Since the seismologist sometimes wants to measure the time of arrival of a wave with an accuracy of a tenth of a second, ordinary clockwork cannot be used for the motor. Clock escapements drive the hands in a series of jerks which may be a fifth or even half a second apart. The steadiest drives for recording drums are synchronous motors, driven by a specially generated

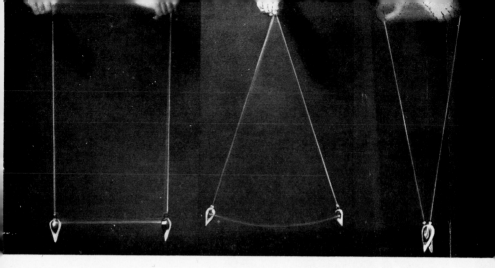

Plate I

RESPONSE OF A SIMPLE PENDULUM, This picture shows the three stages of the experiment described at the beginning of Chapter II.

    (a)   Movement slower than natural period.

    (b)   Movement coincides with natural period.

    (c)   Movement faster than natural period.

Plate II

WOOD-ANDERSON TORSION SEISMOMETER.

    (a)   View from the direction of the recorder.

    (b)   Two short-period suspensions in travelling case. The wires, which have been thickened so as to appear in the photograph, are approximately 1/1000″ thick.

    (c)   Rear view of the seismometer with the cover off and the suspension removed.

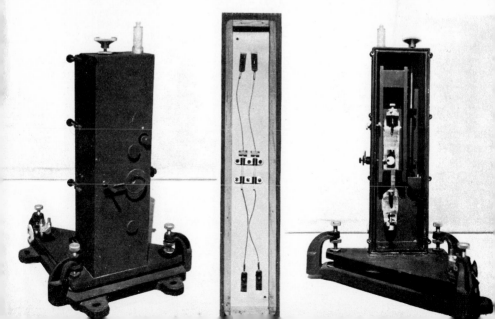

Plate III

**MILNE-SHAW HORIZONTAL PENDULUM SEISMOGRAPH.** The wooden draught cover has been removed, and the recording drum is out of the picture to the left. Beneath the boom at the left hand end, and partly obscured by it, is the small circular recording mirror, which hangs from a pivot on the small rectangular stand, and is connected to the boom by the light L-shaped aluminium coupling. The large mirror fixed to the right hand levelling screw is used in calibrating the instrument.

Plate IV

**BENIOFF VARIABLE RELUCTANCE SEISMOMETER.** This plate shows the vertical component instrument which is shown in cross section in Fig. 6.

instruments. A seismologist generally calls periods of several seconds "long", and those of a second or less "short". Strangely enough, it is the long-period instruments which are used for recording distant earthquakes, although they are made with lower magnifications. This is because of changes which take place in the periods of earthquake waves which travel long distances.

The limit to the magnification which we can use at any particular period is set by small movements of the ground which are called microseisms. They go on all the time, even when there are no earthquakes, and once a seismograph is sensitive enough to show them, an increase in the magnification only makes the recording more and more confused. The most common types of microseism have periods between two and six seconds, so that the long-period instruments are most seriously affected.

A popular long-period seismograph is the Milne Shaw, a direct recording photographic instrument with a period of twelve seconds and a magnification of two hundred and fifty. The pendulum of the Milne Shaw swings on an upper and a lower pivot, rather like a gate, and the movement is magnified by very small and light aluminium levers before being communicated to the mirror (Plate III). It may already have occurred to some readers that although an instrument like this will respond readily to earth movements in one direction, it will be unaffected by movements in a direction at right angles to this, along the line joining the centre of the suspended weight to the hinges. This is quite true, and the well-equipped observatory always has a pair of instruments mounted at right angles; usually, but not always, north and south for one, and east and west for the other. To complete the picture of the ground movement, we need a third instrument, sensitive to up-and-down movements. This has proved to be the most difficult type to construct, but, if we can afford only one instrument, it is probably the most useful to have.

In the vertical seismograph, the only way we can make the

weight free to move up and down is to support it with a spring. This introduces a great many practical difficulties. The spring changes in length and in its elasticity when the temperature changes, and the metal gradually "creeps" as it becomes fatigued. We will take the Galitzin as our example of a vertical instrument, and it will also serve to illustrate the electro-magnetic type (Plate V). The weight is fixed to the boom, pivoted on flat springs at the left-hand end, and kept horizontal by the large vertical coiled spring. The pick-up coil and the large copper vane to provide damping are mounted at the other end. By altering the position of the magnets, the amount of current generated in the coil can be varied, so that the magnification can be adjusted to any desired value, generally between three and four hundred. Galitzin seismographs are often made with very long periods—ten seconds or more for the vertical instrument, and as much as double this for the horizontals. There is a set of these instruments at the Christ-church station with twelve- and twenty-four-second periods respectively.

This by no means exhausts the common types of seismo-graph. The instruments developed by Dr. Benioff in California use a single seismometer to drive galvanometers of different period, and make available some enormous magnifications in the short-period range (Figure 6, Plates IV, VI). In localities free from artificial disturbance and with a low microseism back-ground, they have been operated with magnifications as high as three hundred thousand. The New Zealand Government is installing a set of these instruments at the Apia Observatory in Samoa, and will be sending another set to its Antarctic base in the Ross Sea Dependency for the International Geophysical Year. In New Zealand itself, increasing use is being made of the Willmore, an English instrument with similar characteristics to the Benioff. It suffers somewhat from insufficient damping, and operates only at short periods; but it has the great advan-tage of being portable and relatively inexpensive, so that it can be used for temporary installations and for site testing.

can be adjusted to critical. This seismograph has a magnification of nearly three thousand, and a period of just over three-quarters of a second.

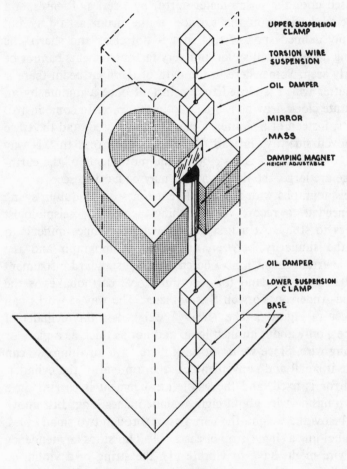

UPPER SUSPENSION CLAMP

TORSION WIRE SUSPENSION

OIL DAMPER

MIRROR

MASS

DAMPING MAGNET
HEIGHT ADJUSTABLE

OIL DAMPER

LOWER SUSPENSION CLAMP

BASE

FIG. 5. WOOD-ANDERSON TORSION SEISMOMETER

Some stations use a modified type with a vane instead of a cylinder. These can be run at a much longer period—up to five or six seconds—but the magnification is then only six or seven hundred. Lower magnifications are usual with all long-period electric current whose frequency is controlled by a tuning fork in a sealed and temperature-controlled enclosure.

Along with the drum goes a recording lamp. Its light is focused upon the seismometer mirror by a series of lenses, and reflected back upon the surface of the drum as a tiny but sharply defined spot. If this spot is not clear and sharp, the timing accuracy will suffer and very fast movements cannot be clearly seen. Somewhere in the path of the light beam there is a shutter which is closed for an instant once a minute by an accurate clock, leaving a brief gap in the trace. In some instruments, instead of a shutter, a glass prism is used, and the trace is moved sideways instead of being blacked out. In this way none of the record is lost, but if the movements of the earthquake are large, the timing marks may be hard to see.

Seismographs with many different times of pendulum swing are needed to record all the things which the seismologist wishes to study. At a first glance, it is sometimes difficult to see the similarity between an actual seismograph and the simple arrangement I have described. The standard instrument used in New Zealand for recording local earthquakes is the Wood-Anderson Torsion Seismometer. The way it works can be seen in Figure 5. The "heavy" weight is a tiny cylinder of copper, only about an inch long, and not as thick as a piece of fencing wire. Since we do not ask it to drive anything, we can make it small and convenient. At the top end of the cylinder, a mirror is fixed, and the whole arrangement is carried on a thin tungsten wire about eight or nine inches long. Just above and below the weight, the wire passes through two small holes, each holding a single drop of castor oil. This stops any tendency the wire might have to vibrate like the string of a violin, so that all the weight can do is to twist back and forth around the wire. On either side of the weight, the poles of a magnet provide eddy-current damping. This magnet is somewhat differently arranged in different models of the instrument, but it can always be moved up and down, and by arranging just the right length of the cylinder to come between the poles the damping kind of wave to picture, but Figure 7 will probably help. Imagine that a long rod is given a sharp tap with a hammer at the left-hand end. Each particle hit by the hammer will move away for an instant and then spring back. When it moves away, it will transmit the force to its neighbour and cause the pulse to travel down the rod. When the pulse gets to the other end, a ball resting against the rod would bounce away to show that it had arrived.

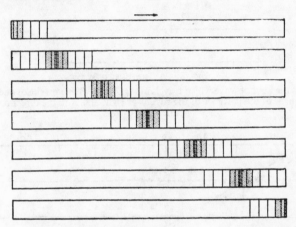

FIG. 7.   A LONGITUDINAL WAVE

This diagram shows how a wave will travel along a rod when it is struck at the left-hand end. The particles of the rod move to and fro in the same direction as the wave is travelling.

In the transverse, or S wave, the particles move at right angles to the direction in which the wave is travelling, exactly like they do in a rope which is fixed at one end and shaken at the other (Figure 8).

These waves do not travel at the same speed. The P wave goes about 8 kilometres (5 miles) in a second, and the S wave only about $4\frac{1}{2}$ kilometres ($2\frac{3}{4}$ miles). (Scientists nearly always measure distances in kilometres, which are about five-eighths of a mile.) This means that the P wave always arrives first, and S lags behind. The further the recorder is from the origin of the earthquake, the bigger the time interval between the arrival of the two waves. If we can identify these two waves on our seismograms, and measure the difference in arrival time, we can work out how far away it was (Figure 9). The further away

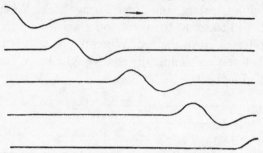

FIG. 8.   A TRANSVERSE WAVE

This is the kind of wave which travels along a rope when you shake one end. The movement of the particles of the rope is at right angles to the direction in which the wave travels.

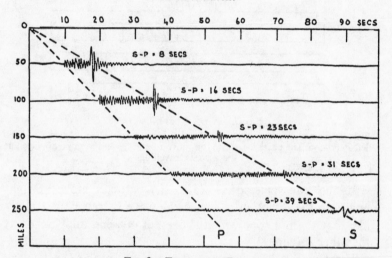

FIG. 9.   FINDING THE DISTANCE

The time interval between the arrival of the longitudinal P wave and the transverse S wave increases with the distance of the origin of the shock.

an earthquake is, the deeper the waves will penetrate into the body of the earth. The deeper they penetrate, the faster they travel, so a simple calculation based on the figures I have just quoted would not be accurate enough. Tables have been drawn up to show the amount of this change, and in practice we can get the result quite quickly.

A single record can tell us the distance accurately, but we can only find the direction if we have three-component

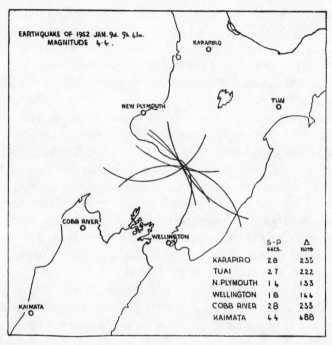

FIG. 10.   EPICENTRE LOCATION

The S–P interval is used to find the distance (Δ) from each station. An arc with this distance as radius, and centred at the station is then drawn. The arcs intersect at the epicentre.

recorders, and there are a number of factors operating to make the estimate of direction less reliable. It is therefore more usual to work out the position of the epicentres by using the distances from a number of stations. This is one of the reasons why seismologists like to send the observatories in other countries copies of their readings as soon as possible. Figure 10 shows how we work out a practical case. On the Wellington record of the earthquake we shall consider, the interval between the

41

arrival of the P and the S wave was 18 sec, and our tables tell us that this corresponds to a distance of 144 km. If we draw a circle with this radius on a map, with the centre at Wellington, the epicentre must be somewhere on this circle. At New Plymouth, the interval was 14 sec, and the corresponding distance is 133 km. When we draw a circle with this radius and its centre at New Plymouth, it will cut the Wellington circle in two points, one near Wanganui, and the other out to sea in Cook Strait. Both these places often have earthquakes, so we can't decide which is the more likely place without a third station. Adding Cobb River to the picture makes it clear that the Wanganui result is the right one, and when we add the readings from Tuai and Karapiro the result is quite certain.

The circles do not all cut in an exact point, for the records are not perfect, and there are small differences in the travel time over different parts of the country which the tables cannot allow for; but when the shock is well recorded, the uncertainty is generally not more than five miles or so. By making special studies and more accurate (and also more lengthy) calculations, we can sometimes locate an important earthquake with an even higher degree of precision.

More often, however, there are complications. When we draw the third circle, we find that it does not go through either of the intersections of the other two. If we can be quite certain that the trouble does not lie in a poor record from one of the stations, or in something wrong with the timing, this is an indication that the focus of the earthquake lies further beneath the surface of the earth than usual; that is to say, we are dealing with a "deep focus earthquake". The distances obtained from S–P intervals are of course distances between the focus and the recording station, not those between the station and the epicentre (Figure 11). It is not difficult to calculate the depth at which the focus must lie to make the circles meet in a point. Figure 12 shows the circles for a deep earthquake under the Bay of Plenty. When we started by assuming that the focus was shallow, it looked as if the epicentre might be off

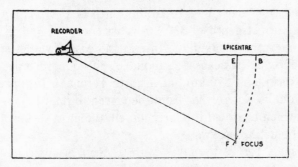

FIG. 11

The length AE is known as the epicentral distance ($\Delta$). In the case when the earth-quake is deep, $\Delta$ is less than the distance AF which would be obtained from the S–P interval. If we draw a circle on the map with its centre at the recorder and radius AF it will pass through the point B instead of through the epicentre.

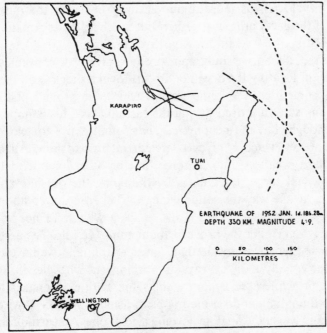

FIG. 12.   EPICENTRE LOCATION

The broken arcs were drawn on the supposition that the earthquake was of normal depth. When tables for the correct depth are used, a satisfactory cut is obtained.

43

the coast near Tolaga Bay, or to the north of East Cape; but when the correct depth of 330 km is assigned, we find that it lies not far from Whakatane. In extreme cases, we get some unusual effects. The deepest earthquake so far recorded in New Zealand was about 570 km under north Taranaki. In this case the earthquake was further from the epicentre than any of the stations which recorded it. Christchurch, the most distant one, is only about 500 km away.

Isoseismals for earthquakes with a deep origin exhibit a different pattern from that of shallow ones, as we saw in Chapter 1. Not only is the pattern comparatively irregular, although the intensity is fairly uniform over a big stretch of country, but sometimes the epicentre lies right outside the boundary of the strongest isoseismal. Further study of this effect should tell us more about the way in which the outer parts of the earth are put together, but much fuller information is needed before we can draw positive conclusions.

The records our seismographs produce give us a convenient method of locating the origin of an earthquake shock; and they tell us something about the way in which the ground at the recording station moved during the earthquake. This is important enough, but the geophysicist has found a use for earthquake waves which is of even greater interest to him. All of my country readers must at some time or other have tried to see how full the water tank is by thumping the outside, and listening to the way the sound changes when you thump above and below the water level. Town readers who have not will probably remember the proverb about empty vessels. The earth is even harder to see inside than a water tank, and we have to look for equally indirect ways of working out what lies inside it. The principle used is almost the same, with earthquakes to do the thumping, and seismographs to listen. Since the P wave is a sound wave, the analogy is quite a close one. An earthquake wave is the only thing we know of which can be sent to explore the very centre of the earth.

Let us suppose that we have collected together all the records

of a very big earthquake. There will be a very big pile of them
—perhaps four or five hundred, even if we don't count all three
components at every recording station. Let us carefully measure
each record, and find the time at which the first movement
arrives. If we list the stations in order of their distance from
the epicentre, we can see that there is a gradual change in the
speed of the journey, and that it increases as the path lies
deeper and deeper in the earth. We should expect this to happen,
because waves travel more rapidly in more rigid material, and
the material deep in the earth will be firmly packed together
by the weight of the material on top of it.

This is a convenient place to note that when the seismologist
deals with distances of more than a few hundred miles, he often
states them in degrees, rather than in miles or even kilometres.
This is like looking at the angle between two lines, one from
the station, and one from the epicentre, which meet at the
centre of the earth. There are 360° right round the earth, and
two points 180° apart are exactly opposite one another. A
degree is about 111 km, or 69 miles. There is a table in the
Appendix to help you convert from one system to the other if
you wish. The advantage of this system of measurement is that
it draws attention to the fact that the earth is a ball, and avoids
any ambiguity between distances measured around the surface
and through the middle.

But let us get back to our big pile of records. As the distance
between the station and the epicentre gets bigger, the size and
clarity of the P movement gets rather worse, until at about
103°, the beginning of the record becomes indistinct. Something is happening to the wave in its travels. This something
continues to happen until about 145°, when the movement
again becomes sharp, but shows by its time of travel that it is
not the same wave we started with. The region in between,
where the wave is indistinct, is called the "shadow zone for
P" (Figure 13).

The reason the shadow zone exists is that at a depth of
2900 km (1800 miles) below the surface, the composition of

45

the earth changes abruptly. The region above this boundary is known as the earth's "mantle" and that below it as the "core". Once the ray from an earthquake penetrates so deeply that it must pass through the core, it will be sharply bent, and emerge at a greater distance than it otherwise would.

The boundary between the mantle and the core is called the "Gutenberg Discontinuity". Even before the work of the

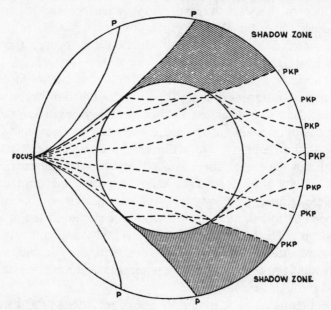

FIG. 13. THE SHADOW ZONE

When P waves cross the boundary between the mantle and the core they are sharply bent. This creates a shadow zone between 103° and 145° from the focus.

pioneer seismologists, various reasons had been put forward for believing that the earth had a denser nucleus in the centre. In 1913, Professor Gutenberg used earthquake waves to give an exact measurement of the depth at which the change took place; and this measurement was one of the first indications of the great part seismology was going to play in exploring the earth's interior.

Everyone is familiar with echoes. When a sound wave meets

an obstacle, part of it will be reflected, and we can he
if there were another source of sound behind the reflecto.
sound wave, passing from one medium to another in which its
speed is different can also be "refracted", or bent. Earthquake
waves of both P and S type can be reflected and refracted in
this way, and in consequence earthquake records become very
complicated. This complication of the records gives the geophysicist further clues to the composition of the earth.

Records of near earthquakes (within about 10° of the recording station) give information about the surface layers of
the earth, but first of all we will look at the simpler construction of the deeper parts, which can be deduced from distant
records. The core is much denser than the mantle of the earth,
and its surface reflects waves and sends them back like echoes.
A reflected P wave is called $P_cP$, and a reflected S wave, $S_cS$.
The small "c" means that the wave reaches the core, but does
not penetrate inside it. The time that a reflected wave takes to
travel is naturally rather longer than that taken by the corresponding wave by the direct path; and it appears as a distinct
pulse on the records. There is a further complication here,
however. When a wave is reflected or refracted, it can change
at the boundary from a P wave to an S wave or vice versa.
This means that instead of there being only two kinds of
reflected wave, there are four—$P_cP$, $S_cS$, $P_cS$, and $S_cP$.

In order to keep track of the different kinds of wave, the
seismologist draws what is known as a "travel-time curve".
This is a graph which shows how long it will take a wave to
travel by each of the possible routes, and there is a line on it
for each separate kind of wave. Figure 14 shows the routes that
the P and S waves and the core reflections take, and the corresponding travel-time curve for these phases. If the distance of
the earthquake is read off along the horizontal line, the time at
which the different pulses will arrive can be read off vertically.

A real seismogram shows many more phases than the half-
dozen I have mentioned. In order to see what other kinds
there are, I shall treat them in "family groups".

The first set are the surface reflections. There is a big difference in density between the air and the rocks of the earth, and conditions are very favourable for reflecting a wave which comes up to the surface from the interior. If a P wave is reflected at a point mid-way between the recording station and the epicentre, it gives rise to a wave called PP, and of course, there is an SS following the same route. Once again, there can be a change of type on reflection, and there are also waves called PS and SP; but in this case the point of reflection is not exactly half-way, although these waves clearly belong to the

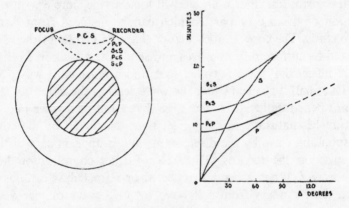

FIG. 14.   CORE REFLECTIONS AND THEIR TRAVEL TIMES

same "family". The length of the P part of PS is the same as that of SP, and similarly for the S part. They will therefore take the same time to travel, although the routes are not the same. These phases are shown in Figure 15.

The number of possible internal reflections is not limited to one. Two reflections are quite common, and there is a whole series of this kind—PPP, SSS, PPS, PSS, SPP, SSP, SPS, and PSP. In the case of a very large earthquake, it is even possible to record PPPP, since the only limit to the complications is the amount of energy available. The energy is not of course divided equally between all the possible phases, and generally speaking, the simpler combinations are the most prominent in the

48

records; but there are some striking exceptions, as the curved layers of the earth can result in focusing effects for certain phases at some particular distances.

The next family of waves is the "core refractions". Earlier in the chapter, we noticed that the direct P wave does not reach beyond about 103° owing to the shadow effect of the core. The first wave to appear on the records at distances beyond this is generally PP, since it does not penetrate so deeply, and is able to avoid the obstacle. This remains the case until about 140°, when a sharp first arrival again makes its appearance. This is

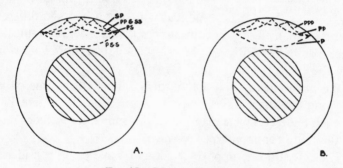

FIG. 15.  SURFACE REFLECTIONS

A. Single reflection with change of type.
B. Single and double reflection.

P once more, but since it has passed through the core of the earth, and was deflected from its path so that it disappeared altogether for nearly 40°, we now call it PKP. What of the rest of the family? If we look for an S wave by the same route, there is a surprise waiting. No transverse waves can get through the core at all unless they first of all change type. This is a most important discovery, and we shall see what it means when we come to discuss the structure of the earth in detail. In writing about waves through the core, then, we only need one letter to describe them. This is K, which stands for *Kern*, the German word for core. All K waves are longitudinal like P. The other members of the family are therefore PKS, SKP,

49

and SKS. There are some rather more distant, but not unimportant relatives which are reflected inside the core itself, such as PKKP and SKKS; and even some which have passed through the core in order to be reflected at the surface of the earth on the opposite side before they return. PKPPKP is the most commonly recorded phase of this type (Figure 16). Trace out these wave paths on the different diagrams, and you will have little difficulty in seeing how the different

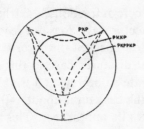

FIG. 16. CORE REFRACTIONS AND INTERNAL REFLECTION

waves are named. If you come across a reference to an unusual one, like PKPPKPPKP, or SKSP, it should be possible to work out the correct path for it.

We have already had a look at a simple travel-time curve, showing the direct waves and the core reflections. Figure 17 is a much more complete diagram of this kind, and includes most of the more common types of wave.

There is still one important class of wave to be considered. These are the surface waves, which are often the most prominent part of a record. They are often called L, or "long" waves, since they oscillate more slowly than either the P or the S type, and they travel round the outside of the earth instead of passing through the interior. Careful study shows that they are a mixture of two different kinds of wave—Love waves and Rayleigh waves, named after their respective discoverers. Both of these men showed mathematically that waves of this kind could exist before they were identified on seismograms. The Love waves are a transverse movement, rather like S, but moving only in a horizontal plane. They are guided around the outside of the earth by continuous reflection between the upper and lower boundaries of the surface layers. They have no vertical component at all.

The Rayleigh waves, on the other hand, have quite a prominent vertical component, and are a kind of "up and over backwards roll", which starts with a push in the direction of travel, then up, back, down, and push again. Both of these waves travel rather more slowly than S, and the Rayleigh wave is rather slower than the Love wave. When we need to distinguish

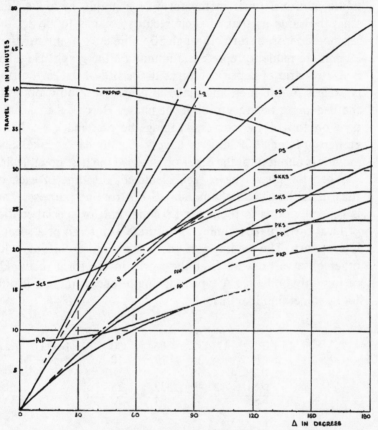

FIG. 17. A TRAVEL-TIME CURVE

The seismologist uses a chart of this kind to help him identify the waves which appear on his records. These curves are for a shallow earthquake, and only the more important arrivals are shown.

them, we call the Love waves $L_q$, from the German *Querwellen*, cross-waves, and the Rayleigh waves $L_r$.

With so many waves to be expected in an earthquake record, how does the seismologist sort them out? Fortunately it is often possible to pick the P and S waves just by looking at the record. This tells how far away the shock is, and reference to tables of travel times helps to fit in the rest of the picture. The method of working most seismologists use is to draw out the tables of travel times in the form of a graph, with the time scale the same as that of their records; that is to say, if the seismograph drum turns through 30 millimetres a minute, then 30 mm are made to represent a minute on the graph. He takes a narrow strip of paper as long as the record of the earthquake he wishes to interpret, and makes a pencil mark on it opposite the beginning of every prominent phase. He can then lay the tape on top of the curves, keeping the first mark on P (or perhaps PP or PKP if it is a very distant earthquake) and moving it about until the other phases give the best possible fit.

When the phases have been identified, the time of each of them must be accurately measured. For routine purposes, this is generally done to the nearest second, but for special studies of local earthquakes, timing as accurate as a tenth of a second is necessary. The readings are then listed, and exchanged with other observatories all over the world in the form of weekly or monthly bulletins. A typical listing in one of these bulletins looks something like this:

|  |  | $h$ | $m$ | $s$ | $\mu$ | $sec$ |  |  |
|---|---|---|---|---|---|---|---|---|
| 1953 Aug. 15 | iP! | 17 | 32 | 06 | 50 | 3 | $\varDelta=83°$ | $h=$N |
|  | PP |  | 34 | 17 | 10 | 7 | $M=7\cdot4$ |  |
|  | $P_cP$ |  | 35 | 51 |  |  |  |  |
|  | e(S) |  | 40 | 33 | 75 | 5 |  |  |
|  | SS |  | 42 | 04 | 20 | 8 |  |  |
|  | $L_q$ |  | 46·3 |  |  |  |  |  |
|  | $L_r$ |  | 47·1 |  |  |  |  |  |
|  | Max |  | 53 |  | 250 | 18 |  |  |

There are a few symbols here which have not yet been explained. When a phase has a sharp beginning, we prefix its symbol with an i, which stands for impulsive; and if it is very sharp indeed, we may even follow it with an exclamation mark. On the other hand, a movement may be so small, or the background of microseisms so heavy, that it is not easy to judge just what particular instant is the true beginning of the particular phase. Such a reading is labelled e, for emergent. Sometimes a sharp P phase appears to be preceded by a slight "curtsey", or small movement of the trace beforehand. In such a case the phase is written ei.

All phases will not agree precisely with a set of theoretical travel-time curves, and even a good seismologist is frequently uncertain of the true identity of some of the phases on his records. If he is not sure of the interpretation, he puts the name of the phase in brackets. On the other hand, a question mark means that the movement may not have anything to do with the earthquake at all, and could just as well be a prominent microseism, somebody working in the cellar, or an insect in the works. The column headed $\mu$ (the Greek letter mu) is a measurement of how much the ground moved when that particular phase arrived. $\mu$ stands for microns, or thousandths of a millimetre, so it is obvious that the movements are not as a rule very big. The column headed "sec" is the period, or time of swing of the ground movement. The final column gives the estimated distance ($\Delta$) in degrees, the depth of focus ($h$) in kilometres, or "N" for normal depth; and the instrumental magnitude ($M$) of the shock which is explained in Chapter 7. Individual stations vary their procedures slightly, but the main pattern is always very similar, and there is no difficulty in following bulletins in Greek, Russian, Turkish, or Japanese!

To conclude the chapter, which is already a long one, let us review the characteristics of some typical records at different distances (Figures 18–22). Up to about 5°, the main phases are P and S, the periods are short, and there are no obvious surface waves. From 20° to 40°, P, S, and L can be clearly picked out, and the reflected phases PP and SS are usually present. The main S phase remains prominent in records up to 90° or 100°, but round about 80° there is a certain complication of the record resulting from the almost simultaneous

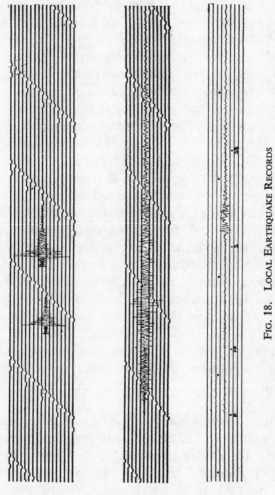

FIG. 18. LOCAL EARTHQUAKE RECORDS

Three Wood-Anderson seismograms of shocks at increasing distances. A and B were made at Wellington, and C at Karapiro.

A. Two minor shocks in Cook Strait. 1950, Feb. 1    $\Delta = \frac{1}{4}°$    $M = 3\frac{1}{4}$
B. Western Hawkes Bay. 1950, Mar. 28    $\Delta = 2 \cdot 9°$    $M = 5\frac{1}{2}$
C. Kermadec Islands Region. 1953, Feb. 19    $\Delta = 9°$    $M = 6\frac{1}{4}$

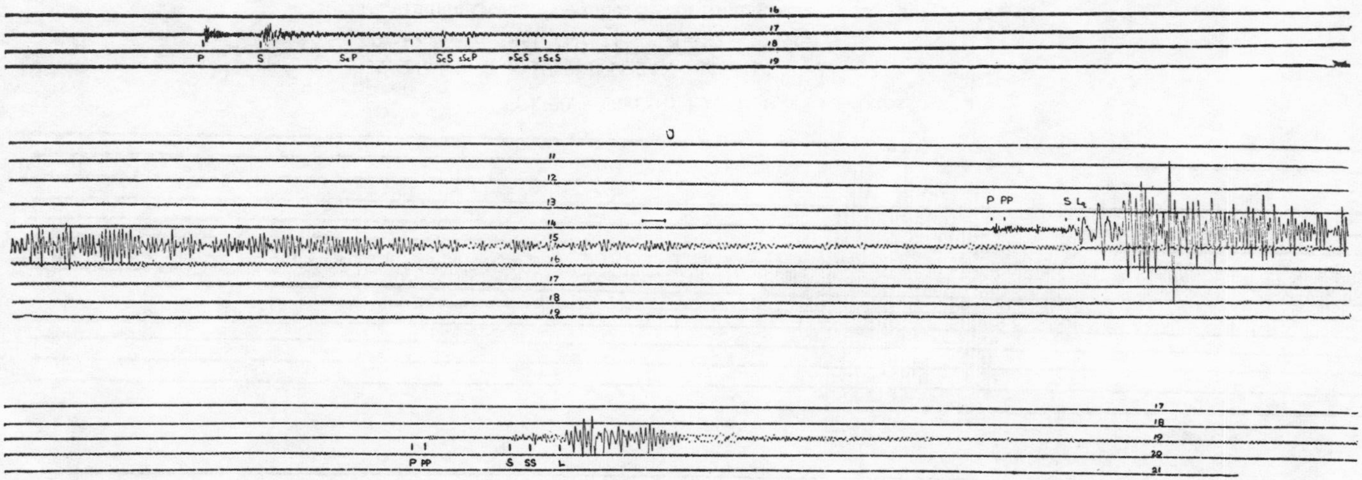

FIG. 19.  DEEP AND SHALLOW EARTHQUAKE RECORDS

Three Wellington Milne-Shaw seismograms of shocks at approximately the same distance. Note the short periods and the absence of surface waves in the deep earthquake, and also the prominence of ScS, a reflection from the boundary of the core.

A. Kermadec Islands Region. 1951, Aug. 28    $\Delta=15°$    $M=6\frac{3}{4}$    Depth 625 km.

B. Tonga Region. 1952, May 4    $\Delta=20°$    $M=6\frac{1}{4}$    Normal depth.

C. 650 miles west of Macquarie Is. 1952, Feb. 8    $\Delta=22°$    $M=6\frac{1}{4}$    Normal depth.

55

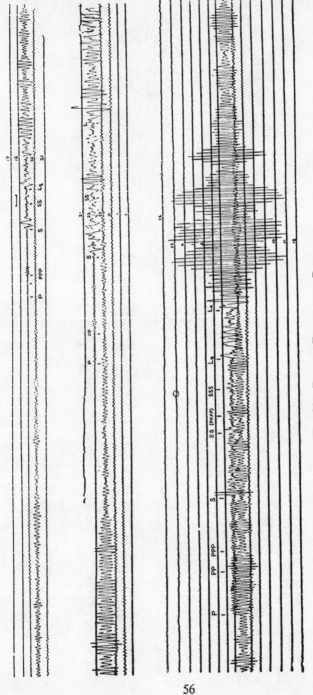

FIG. 20.  DISTANT EARTHQUAKE RECORDS

A. New Britain. 1952, Dec. 24    $\Delta=41°$    $M=7\frac{1}{4}$

B. Formosa. 1951, Oct. 21    $\Delta=82°$    $M=7\frac{1}{2}$

C. Indian Ocean, 900 miles SE. of Madagascar    $\Delta=86°$    $M=6\frac{1}{4}$

56

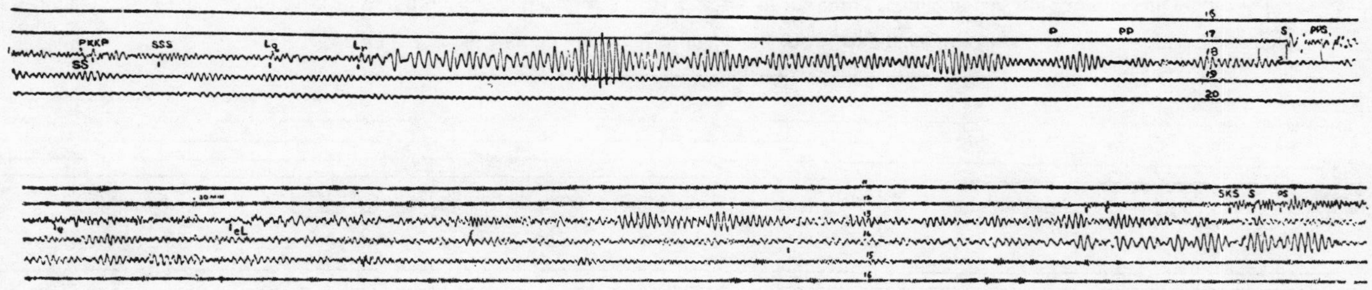

FIG. 21. DISTANT EARTHQUAKE RECORDS

The early part of the latter record is lost in the background of microseisms. The S wave of an aftershock can be seen just before 14 h, and the surface waves follow about ten minutes later.

A. Kurile Islands. 1951, Nov. 6    $\Delta=91°$    $M=7\frac{1}{4}$
B. Mojave Desert, California, U.S.A.    $\Delta=97°$    $M=7\frac{1}{2}$

57

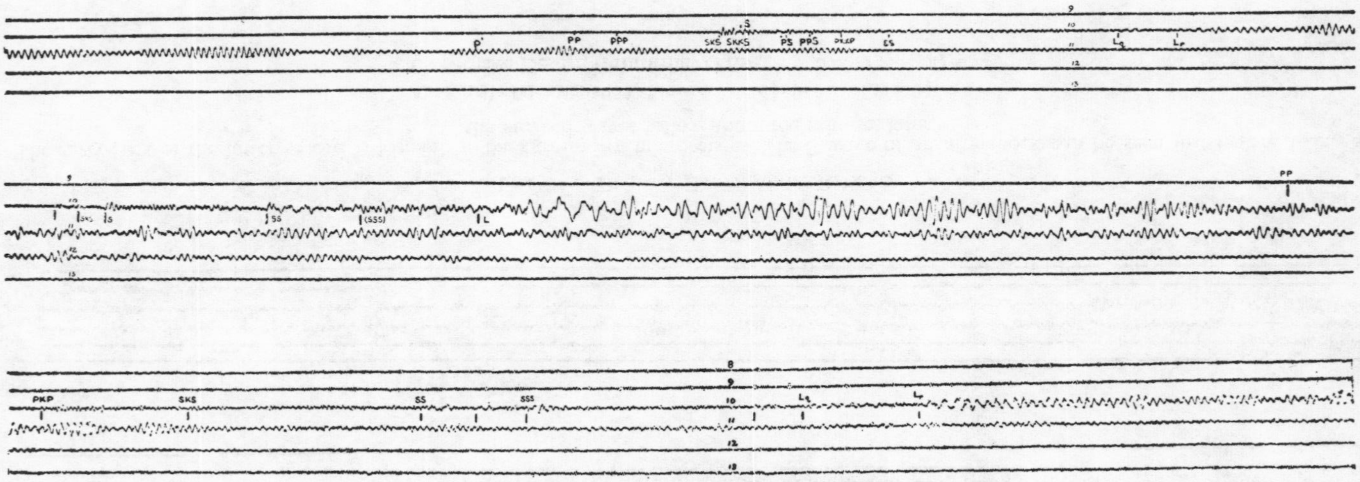

Fig. 22. Earthquake Records inside and outside the Shadow Zone.

At distances rather more than half-way round the earth, the effect of the shadow of the core becomes apparent. The shock in record A is outside the shadow zone, and P still appears on the record. In B, PP is the first clear movement, and in C, the P reappears as PKP after passage through the core.

A. Guerrero, Mexico. 1951, Dec. 28    $\Delta = 99°$    $M = 7\frac{1}{2}$
B. Eastern Tibet, north of Lhasa. 1951, Nov. 18    $\Delta = 106°$    $M = 7\frac{1}{4}$
C. Mid-Atlantic Ocean. 1951, July 18    $\Delta = 130°$    $M = 6\frac{3}{4}$

arrival of SKS, S, and $S_cS$, so that wrong identification is only too easy. Beyond this distance PS and PSP begin to show quite clearly. Records in the shadow zone (105° to 143°) present quite a changed appearance. Unless the earthquake is large, there will be gaps between the phases in which little but microseisms can be distinguished. The first phase is generally PP, followed by PPP or PKS; and PS and PSP are prominent. SKKS is stronger than SKS. At very great distances, "textbook" records are seldom obtained, but PKP is well established as the first movement. The records are also complicated by phases which have gone the long way round, and traversed more than half the earth.

In all record interpretation, experience plays a considerable part, and in the case of a difficult record, it is often wiser to wait for further information before attempting to measure the record in detail. In any case, interpretations are revised when the information comes to hand. To help in this task, the United States Coast and Geodetic Survey maintains a very valuable service. A selection of large observatories has undertaken to send them the readings of all well-recorded shocks by urgent cable. The survey uses these readings to work out an approximate origin time and epicentre as soon as possible. The precision of these preliminary epicentres is amazingly high, and within forty-eight hours of an important shock, special postcards have been printed and sent by airmail to interested observatories. This is an effective piece of international co-operation, not the least remarkable aspect of which is its speed. Certain other organisations, such as the Jesuit Seismological Association at Saint Louis, and the Bureau Central Séismologique International at Strasbourg, maintain epicentre services of less speed but improved accuracy. Many observatories assume the responsibility for specially intense study of some limited area. In Wellington, for example, an attempt is made to keep the South-West Pacific and the Tonga-Kermadec Trench in particular under special observation; as well as providing an epicentre for every earthquake which is actually felt within New Zealand. Local areas in which the seismicity can be studied in detail are rare, and the network in California is probably the only one which surpasses the New Zealand installation for work of this kind.

Something has already been said about deep focus earthquakes. Normal shocks occur within the crust of the earth; that is to say, down to about 20 or 30 miles below the surface. About thirty years ago, Professor Turner showed that some of the earthquakes reported to the International Seismological Summary had foci at greater depths. The deepest ones so far recorded occur near the Celebes Islands and to the north-east of New Zealand near the Tonga-Kermadec Trench, and are almost 700 km down. If a shock has a deep focus, it alters the character of a record quite considerably. Surface waves are recorded only from the shallower ones, and the records are complicated by the appearance of a new set of reflected phases.

It will be recalled that a P or an S phase can be reflected near the mid-point of its path to give rise to the phases PP and SS. When the shock originates below the surface, there is also a

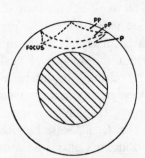

FIG. 23. REFLECTIONS NEAR THE EPICENTRE IN DEEP FOCUS EARTHQUAKES

reflection very close to the epicentre. Because its path from the focus to the surface is so short, we denote this first leg of the journey by a small letter, so that the phases are called pP (read as "little p P"), sP, pS, sS, and so on. A glance at the diagram (Figure 23) will show that the time of travel for pP or sS will not be very different from that of P or S. Each phase in the record can therefore appear double or triple, and the inexperienced observer can mistake the record for that of two earthquakes which have become superimposed because they happened within a few seconds of one another. These phases give us one convenient method of working out the focal depth.

Core reflections such as $S_cS$ are also helpful, and in New Zealand a good deal of attention is paid to the phase $sS_cS$. We are also fortunate that at the antipodes, in Europe, there is a fairly dense network of recording stations which can observe the phase PKP from New Zealand shocks. This gives another valuable check upon the depth.

# CHAPTER FOUR

# The First By-Product

PROSPERO: . . . deeper than did ever plummet sound . . .
SHAKESPEARE: *The Tempest*

THERE is a story told about Sir J. J. Thomson, the discoverer of the electron, which should be more widely known. He was being asked, as many scientists are, what use could be made of his discoveries. "Let us suppose", he said, "that at the time of the Franco-Prussian war, the nations had become alarmed at the great number of wounds in which pieces of bullet were still lodged, and could not be located; and that when the peace treaties were signed, the nations had agreed to offer a large premium to be paid to the man who could devise the most efficient method of finding these foreign bodies. What would have happened? Probing would have become a fine art, and the human body a pincushion—but we should not have discovered X-rays."

There are many morals which might be drawn from this tale. If the men who founded the science of seismology had been of a "practical" turn of mind, they might well have dismissed the study of the structure of the earth as less important than the early development of some system of earthquake-proof building construction, or concentrated a meagre allowance of funds on the problem of earthquake prediction. If that had happened, we might still be without the most directly useful technique which seismology has developed—that of seismic prospecting. This, however, is to begin the story in the middle.

In 1910, there was published the study of an earthquake in Kulpa Valley, Croatia, in October of the previous year. The author, A. Mohorovičić, noticed that records made at stations close to the epicentre did not show the simple P and S phases,

62

but had in addition a secondary movement following each of them. This, he suggested, could be explained if the outermost portion of the earth were supposed to consist of a crust some 60 km in thickness, resting on top of the mantle. As we shall see, there have been great arguments about this figure, and seismologists are still discussing the nature of the outer portion of the earth; but Mohorovičić had shown them the method of using local earthquakes to explore it. How does the method work?

Suppose we have a series of seismographs spread out along a line from the origin of the earthquake, assumed to be at the

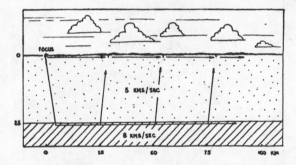

FIG. 24. THE ORIGIN OF CRUSTAL PULSES IN NEAR EARTHQUAKE RECORDS

surface of the earth, and that there are about 25 km of crust (probably a more accurate figure than 60) overlying the mantle of the earth (Figure 24). Let us further assume that a P wave travels with a speed of about 5 km/sec in the crust, and 8 km/sec in the mantle. At a station close to the epicentre, the first wave to arrive will be the slow one, which is called $P_g$. This travels directly along the path between the focus and the station, so that if it is 50 km long, the wave will take 10 sec for the trip. At 25 km it will take 5 sec, and at 100 km it would take 20 sec. We can show this on a simple graph like the ones we drew for the waves deep in the earth in the last chapter (Figure 25). In addition to $P_g$, a second wave, called $P_n$, can be recorded. This travels through the mantle for most of its path, and is the same

63

wave that we called P when we were talking about distant earthquakes.

At a distance of 50 km, the $P_n$ wave goes down to the base of the crust (25 km) at $P_g$ speed, which takes about 5 sec (really more, as it goes down a slanting path instead of a vertical one), and then along the 50 km at 8 km/sec, say about 6 sec. Finally it comes up again at the slow speed, taking another 5 sec for the journey, and bringing the total time to 16 sec for the whole trip. This is 6 sec longer than $P_g$ takes for the same journey

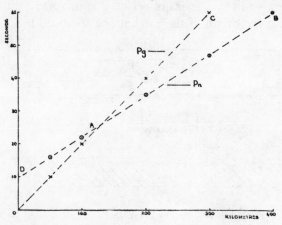

FIG. 25.   TRAVEL TIME OF CRUSTAL PULSES

Travel time of crustal pulses in a model crust in which a 25-km thickness of material, in which the velocity of P is 5 km/sec, overlies a mantle in which the velocity is 8 km/sec.

and so it appears on the records as a later pulse. If the recording station is 100 km away, $P_n$ still needs 10 sec to go down and come up again, but it only takes 12 sec to do the main part of the trip. This makes a total of 22 sec, so that $P_n$ is now only 2 sec behind $P_g$. For a path 200 km long, $P_g$ takes 40 sec. $P_n$ takes only 25 sec in the mantle, so that even if we add 10 sec for the up-and-down journey, the total is only 35 sec. This means that $P_n$ is now the first pulse to arrive, and it will continue to gain steadily. The results can be summarised as follows:

64

Plate V

GALITZIN ELECTROMAGNETIC SEISMOGRAPH. This is the simplest form of the vertical component instrument. The copper damping vane moves between the poles of the outer set of magnets at the right, whilst the pick-up coil moves between those of the inner set. Improved models have additional springs to reduce the effect of temperature variations upon the stability.

Plate VI

BENIOFF VARIABLE RELUCTANCE SEISMOMETER. In the horizontal instrument, seen here, the mass has been divided into two parts, and the pick-up assembly placed between them. There is of course no central spring to correspond with the one in the vertical component instrument.

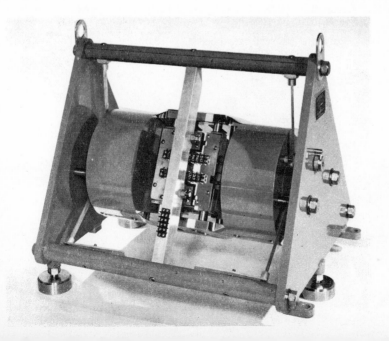

Plate VII

**GEOPHYSICAL PROSPECTING.** *A. The Explosion.* As a rule, the small charges used are exploded at the bottom of a drill hole through comparatively hard material, and there is not so large a blast as this. In this case, the explosion had to be fired in sand, because the depth of the underlying rock was to be calculated. This work was a necessary preliminary to extending the Rongotai Aerodrome, Wellington.

Plate VIII

**GEOPHYSICAL PROSPECTING.** *B. Laying the Spread.* The Century seismic truck of the N.Z. Department of Scientific and Industrial Research at work near Taupo. The large reel carries half a mile or more of multi-cored cable, which brings the output of up to 24 separate geophones back to the recording camera inside the truck. As it drives slowly along, paying out the cable, the geophones are dropped overboard and connected to take-out points 100 feet apart by an operator walking behind.

Plate IX

GEOPHYSICAL PROSPECTING. *C. The Recording Camera and Amplifiers.* Inside the truck, twelve identical sets of amplifiers and filters are placed on each side of the central recording camera, which contains twenty-four sensitive but robust galvanometers. The operator can see whether the geophones are working correctly by watching the traces through an inspection window.

Plate X

GEOPHYSICAL PROSPECTING. *D. The Photographic Equipment.* This is another view of the inside of the recording truck. Developing chemicals are held in tanks with watertight lids. The cupboard nearest the camera contains a radio transmitter and receiver, with which the operator can talk to the shot firer. The shot instant is radioed back to the truck, and automatically registered on the record. The operator is holding a typical record.

Plate XI

THE GEOLOGICAL COLUMN. Here is a sequence of alternating sandstones and siltstones with the strata still lying horizontally as they did when first deposited. But disruption has already started, as shown by the minor faulting on the right.

Plate XII

THE GEOLOGICAL COLUMN DISRUPTED. This contorted and fractured limestone at White Rock, in the eastern Wairarapa, gives an idea of the way rock can behave under sufficient heat and pressure. It would be difficult to work out in detail all that has happened to this formation.

| $\varDelta$ | $P_g$ | $P_n$ |
|---|---|---|
| 50 km | 10 sec | 16 sec |
| 100 | 20 | 22 |
| 200 | 40 | 35 |
| 300 | 60 | 47 |
| 400 | 80 | 60 |

Of course, in the real earth, things do not work out in such nice round figures, but the principle is the same, and the values are approximately right.

Mohorovičić had to look at this problem the other way round, as he did not know the speeds of the waves or the thickness of the crust to begin with. Let us look at the problem from his point of view. If we can get a good set of records of a local earthquake, and measure the time at which the pulses arrive, we can draw a graph like the one in Figure 25. The line OAC allows us to work out the speed of $P_g$, and DAB gives us that of $P_n$. The distance at which they intersect depends upon the thickness of the upper layer, and upon the relative speeds, so it is possible to use them to calculate the thickness.

In a practical case, there are always further difficulties. The records will not all be perfect: some of them may not have sufficiently accurate timing; some of the phases may be emergent; and we may not have determined the epicentre sufficiently well to give good values for the station distances. A further complication was soon found. In most parts of the world there are more than two pulses recorded, which means that there are more than two layers. Not only is this so, but the variations in the speed of the wave in the various layers is so great that it was obvious that different seismologists were not all measuring the same thing. For a time, new layers were added to the earth's crust at a rate of about one a month!

Perhaps the measurements were faulty as a result of the poor data available? If only there were more seismograph stations! If only they had better clocks! If only we knew where and when an earthquake was to happen! There was one way out. An artificial explosion could be accurately timed, and located. It would have none of the disadvantages of an earthquake, and a special network of stations could be set up to record it. This was where the practical men became interested. The base of the crust was not the only layer buried in the earth which men were eager to know about. Geologists working for the large oil companies wanted some way in which they could check their guesses about the way the strata they mapped at the surface of the earth behaved at greater depths, without the costly trouble of drilling. Could there be a trap in the folds a few thousand feet underground which might contain oil? The answer could be obtained with a small explosive charge, and a couple of dozen portable seismographs. Soon the big oil companies were providing money for geophysical research and for the development of more convenient instruments.

The seismometers used by the modern oil prospector are known as geophones, and are more rugged and smaller than the ones used in observatories. There are two factors which make this possible. The first is that they can be made with short periods, since they are to be used close to the source of the vibrations; and secondly, valve amplifiers can be used to boost their output. Amplifiers are not generally used in observatory seismographs, as there would always be risk of a burned-out valve or some other failure interrupting the record. In a modern prospecting set-up, such as the Century truck used by the New Zealand Geophysical Survey (Plates VII–X), there are twenty-four geophones, which can be attached at intervals of about 100 ft to a cable which is run out from a drum at the rear of the truck. The amplifiers can be arranged so as to turn the geophone into a pick-up of almost any characteristic likely to be useful. The twenty-four light beams from the twenty-four galvanometers are arranged to record side by side on a strip of photographic paper about four inches wide. The truck carries full facilities for developing the records; and radio equipment enables the operator to keep in touch with the shot-firer, and automatically records the instant of the shot on the photographic paper along with the galvanometer traces. A special built-in-tuning-fork unit puts precise timing marks on the paper at $\frac{1}{100}$-sec intervals.

The explosion is generated by a small plug of gelignite lowered down a 20- or 30-ft hole. The hole is necessary to get below the surface soil and weathered layers of the earth, so that the force of the explosion can be communicated to the ground as efficiently as possible. A second truck carries drilling equipment, and a third has water tanks to supply "lubrication" to the point of the drill.

Although oil companies have been responsible for much of the expenditure which has been needed for developing modern prospecting equipment, there are many other uses to which it can be put. In New Zealand, seismic surveys have been used to examine the dam-sites for our great hydro-electric power stations, in connection with the search for geothermal power at Wairakei, and in the exploration of coal and other mineral resources. In this way, seismology is giving the answers to many problems which can scarcely have occurred to the early pioneers of earthquake study.

The technique I have described is known to the prospector as "refraction shooting". In recent years it has been supplanted for many purposes by the reflection method, which is in many ways more straightforward, since it uses a direct record of the echoes from the boundaries between the rock strata beneath the surface. The geophones used to record reflections can be placed nearer to the shot point than those used in refraction measurements, and this saves a great deal of time in laying cable for the geophone spread. Early seismic prospectors were forced to use the refraction method, because their geophones and amplifiers were only able to record the time of arrival of the first impulse with any clarity. By using modern geophones in conjunction with amplifiers and filters of known frequency characteristics, and automatic volume control to limit the effect of the first movement, the arrival of subsequent reflections can be clearly identified on the record (Figure 26).

As the petroleum resources on the continent of America have been more and more exploited, the oil companies have turned their attention to the possibility that further deposits may lie beneath the waters of the Gulf of Mexico. It was obviously unsatisfactory for them to have to limit their geological and geophysical studies to the neighbouring dry land. In consequence, equipment for undertaking seismic surveys at sea is at

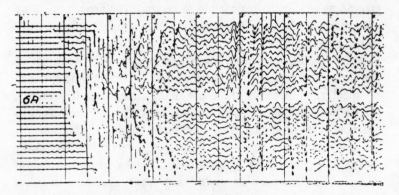

FIG. 26.   REFLECTION PROSPECTING

This is a portion of a record made near Dannevirke by the seismic unit of the Geophysical Survey, N.Z.D.S.I.R. The shot was fired at the centre of a spread of 24 geophones. After the arrival of the direct wave (on the left), the record is confused for a short time, and then reflected waves are received from the boundaries between the buried strata. The timing lines are at intervals of $\frac{1}{100}$ sec, so that the part of the record reproduced occupies less than a second.

present being developed. The work is meeting with considerable success, and like most new techniques it will bring with it a host of new scientific problems to be solved, as well as the solution to others. Hydrographers have found that seismic methods can give them valuable information about the sea bottom; and the way in which sound waves are transmitted in water is being intensively studied, not only for the purpose of submarine detection, but also as a method by which aviators who have crashed can signal their position to shore listening stations.

# CHAPTER FIVE

# *Down to Rock Bottom*

The earth doth like a snake renew
Her winter weeds outworn.
SHELLEY: *Hellas*

AS far as we can see at the surface, the globe on which we live is made of rock. It stands in huge masses to form mountain ranges; the beds of the rivers are strewn with boulders; the sand of the beaches is ground-up rock. There are many different kinds of rock, and everyone is familiar with the names of some of them—granite, basalt, limestone, and so on. Before the nature of earthquakes can be understood, we need a clear picture of the way in which rocks are formed, and how they are changed by the forces of nature.

All the rocks which are found at the surface of the earth have been grouped into three main classes—sedimentary, igneous, and metamorphic. By far the most plentiful of these groups is the first. Sedimentary rocks cover about three-quarters of the total land surface, and their average depth has been estimated at about a mile. These rocks are the result of a most important geological process which goes on continually. It would be wrong to think of the geologist as a man who is only concerned with long-dead fossils and things which happened millions of years ago. He is probably more aware of the constant change and renewal of his surroundings than other people. Every rock which is exposed at the surface of the earth, or "outcrops" as it is called, is subjected to weathering, which gradually breaks it up into small fragments. In high mountain regions, alternate freezing and thawing makes the process a comparatively rapid one; but the chemical action of water on the material of the rock, the blasting of wind-driven sand, and

69

grinding by glacier ice all play a part in the process of disintegration.

Once the rock mass has been reduced to small enough fragments, it is carried away and sorted by wind and water. Sometimes, the material can be moved bodily by the current; and in times of flood, the amount of material shifted can be very great; sometimes the process is the gentle one of solution; but in the end the result is the same—the rocks of the mountain ranges are moved gradually to the coast. Material carried along rivers and watercourses enlarges the channel by scouring the bed and eroding the banks. Every year the Mississippi River moves more than four hundred million tons of material. During transportation, further breaking up occurs, and the angular chips which make up the shingle slides of the Southern Alps become the rounded gravel in the river beds of the Canterbury Plains. Along the coast, waves take a hand, and the broken and pulverised material comes to rest on the sea bottom, where it is able to consolidate under the pressure of the superimposed material to form new rocks.

The nature of the new rock which is formed will depend upon the type of material which is being deposited. For example, very fine particles cannot be expected to come to rest in water which is running swiftly, or which is churned up by breaking waves. The details of this process have naturally been very carefully studied, but for our purposes, it is sufficient to notice its importance. As time goes on, and more and more material accumulates, the distribution of currents will be altered, and the depth of the sea will change. The supply of weathered material may now come from a different part of the mountain range, and be different in texture or chemical composition from that originally deposited. The rocks formed on the sea floor consequently lie in a series of superimposed layers.

Material brought down by the rivers is not the only possible source of the sediment needed for rock formation. Limestone, for example, is a most important exception, although it is still a sedimentary rock. In this case, the material deposited originates in the sea itself, particularly where it is warm and shallow, and consists mainly of the shells and skeletons of dead sea creatures which sink to the sea floor. When there is no admixture of other material we get a pure chalk or limestone; but under certain conditions it may merely serve as a kind of natural cement to bind material brought down by the rivers, or transported along the coast by ocean currents.

The superimposed layers of rock which result from the process of sedimentation are called "strata" (Plate XI). They have roughly parallel surfaces, and vary in thickness according to the rate at which the material accumulated, and the time for which the deposition continued. In a series of undisturbed strata, the oldest rocks will lie at the bottom, and the youngest at the top. Sedimentary rocks often surround the shells or skeletons of animals and plants, which become buried in the sediments when they are being accumulated. These remains are known as fossils; and if they are well enough preserved to let us identify them, they give an important clue to the age of the rock. The types of creature living together have changed throughout geological history, so that if we find a similar set of fossils in two different rocks we can be fairly sure that they were laid down at about the same time. For example, a sandstone from Wanganui might contain the same fossils as those in another rock from Hawkes Bay, enabling us to overlap the series of strata observed in the two places. In this way we can extend the complete "geological column". This is the name we give to the full sequence of strata from the very oldest to the most recent; and this sequence gives an indication of how long ago a given geological event took place. It is not easy to say how long a given geological period lasted, but good estimates can now be made by using measurements of the amount of radioactive material in the rocks. A schoolboy who knows the names of England's kings and queens in their right order knows that something which happened in the reign of Charles II took place before something in the reign of George IV, even if he doesn't know the dates of each reign. If he has a rough idea of the average length of a reign, he can make a reasonable estimate of the number of years involved. In the same way, a geologist knows that a Cambrian rock is older than a Jurassic one, and that he has got his events in the right order, even if he is uncertain of the speed of the complete process. A list of the

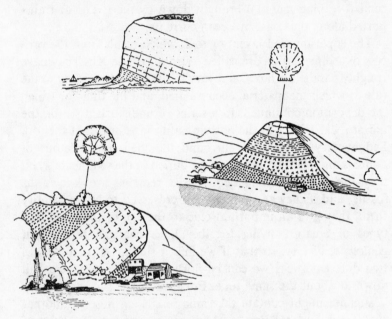

FIG. 27. THE GEOLOGICAL COLUMN

The complete geological column is pieced together by comparing the fossil sequence in the strata of many separate localities. Remember that the fossil determines the *age* of the rock, and not its composition. A limestone in one locality may have been formed at the same time as a sandstone somewhere else.

geologist's periods with recent estimates of their lengths is given in the Appendix.

It is seldom that more than a limited section of the geological column is to be found in one place, so that the deciphering of the whole story of the earth is a laborious process. Professor Cotton has likened it to an attempt to assemble a complete book from a great pile of damaged copies which have been torn into groups of a few pages (Figure 27).

In many parts of the world, but not in New Zealand, volcanoes have long ceased to be active; and the ordinary dweller in those lands might be surprised to learn that the peaceful hillside near his home was once the scene of showers of hot ash. In these localities, as well as in places where volcanic activity still continues, the second important type of rock is found. These rocks are called "igneous", a name which indicates their fiery origin. Sometimes they actually came to the surface of the earth in their hot condition, and flowed as lava from some volcanic vent; in other cases they have forced their way upwards through the underground strata, only to solidify and remain buried until erosion exposes them at the surface. In either case, they were once hot enough to flow with a greater or less degree of freedom, until they cooled or crystallised into their present form. Since they must once have been deep in the earth, they are of great interest to the geophysicist, as they help to confirm his deductions about the nature of the earth's interior.

The third main class, the metamorphic rocks, occupies an intermediate position between the other two classes. In its original form, a metamorphic rock may have belonged to either, but deep burial and subjection to heat and pressure, the behaviour during cooling and crystallisation, or the heat from a nearby igneous intrusion have so changed its characteristics that it is necessary to describe it as a new kind of rock. The divisions between our classes are not quite clear cut, but they are nevertheless very useful distinctions.

Changes on the earth's surface are not a one-way process. The rocks of our land areas, igneous, metamorphic, and sedimentary, would seem from the account I have given to be alike destined to erosion, transportation by rivers, and deposition on some distant sea floor. This is only half the story. Since three-quarters of the land area is composed of sedimentary rocks, it is obvious that at some stage the ocean bed must once again become dry land. This is mainly the result of the process known as "orogenesis", or mountain-building. The details of this process are still very speculative, and we shall have to return to them again, but it seems probable that the building of a mountain range begins with the filling of a shallow basin with

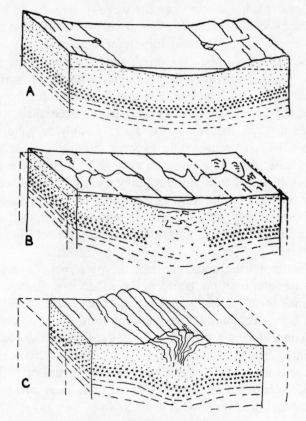

FIG. 28. MOUNTAIN BUILDING
A. Sediment from the land is deposited in a shallow sea.
B. A geosyncline is formed.
C. Compression of the crust raises a chain of fold mountains.

a great mass of sediment (Figure 28). As the sediment accumulates, the supporting floor of the basin is further deformed and depressed. This structure is called a "geosyncline". Because the floor of the geosyncline is forced to a greater depth than its original one, it is weakened by the higher temperature. Under

74

the influence of compressional forces in the earth's crust, the prism of sediment is folded and buckled, and dry land appears in the form of a new mountain range. By this time, the old continent which was the source of the sediment will have been largely eroded away, and the new mountain range will greatly alter the drainage pattern. Erosion will proceed as before, possibly contributing to the formation of a new geosyncline and a further period of mountain building. In this way a cyclic process comes into action, affording justification for the claim of an earlier geologist that there is "no trace of a beginning, and no prospect of an end".

One result of mountain building is the widespread disruption of the geological column to which I have referred. Although we can find fairly extended sequences of strata, they have to be looked for carefully, and the rocks are often found bent and folded into strange shapes (Plate XII), cracked and shattered by the magnitude of the forces at work upon them. The process is a slow one, but the results are far-reaching. One of the consequences is the periodical occurrence of earthquakes, but before we discuss this, we must pay some attention to the constitution of the earth at greater depths than those with which the geologist habitually deals.

# CHAPTER SIX

## *Inside the Earth*

Our souls, whose faculties can comprehend
The wondrous Architecture of the world.
CHRISTOPHER MARLOWE: *Tamburlaine*

**B**Y the methods which have been outlined in previous chapters, the seismologist is able to build up a picture of the construction of the earth right to its centre. It is still lacking in detail, but it is clear enough to throw considerable light upon the origin of the earth and the other members of the sun's family.

The earth is a ball, 7900 miles in diameter, revolving about the sun at a distance of some 92 million miles. By drilling, we have only penetrated about three miles of the four thousand miles which lie between us and the centre of the earth. The rest of our knowledge has been laboriously reconstructed from indirect evidence, and most of this has been provided by the seismologist.

There are three main divisions to the earth: a thin skin called the crust, some tens of miles in thickness, enclosing two regions of roughly equal size, the mantle, and the core. We are most familiar with the upper portion of the crust, to which we have direct access, so that it is there we will begin our description, and work downwards to the centre.

Not so many years ago, it was generally believed that the earth originated as a very hot body, and was in the process of gradually cooling off. It was thought that the outside must have cooled first, and that a molten interior still lay some little distance beneath the surface. Hence the following dialogue in Büchner's play *Danton's Death*:

FIRST CITIZEN: You're not frightened, surely?

76

SECOND CITIZEN: Well you see, sir, the earth has a very thin crust—very thin, sir—very thin. I always fancy you might drop right through if you stepped into a hole like that. One has to tread very carefully indeed, sir, very carefully indeed. You might break through . . .

Today, we have a clearer idea of the behaviour of materials under heat and pressure, and we can treat puddles with less circumspection. It is quite true that the earth gets hotter and hotter as we go deeper and deeper inside it—about one degree Fahrenheit for every fifty feet down, and although we have only been able to take our measurements to a depth of a mile or two, we can be fairly confident that the temperature will go on increasing to a considerably greater depth. It takes no great imagination to realise that a point will soon be reached at which rocks of the kind we meet at the surface would melt, and become somewhat like the lava which flows out of volcanoes. At a depth of 30 miles, the temperature would be about 1500°F. There is, however, an objection to this picture. So great is the weight of the surface rocks that melting cannot take place. Nevertheless, at some definite depth, all the rocks lose their individual identity, and become fused together into one great mixture. Perhaps the best way to think of the physical condition of the rocks at this depth is to liken them to solid pitch. Even if it is so solid that it can be shattered by a hammer blow, it will still flow and spread if you leave a lump on the bench overnight. If we treat it gently, it behaves as a liquid; but if we apply sudden forces to it, it behaves like a brittle solid.

The depth at which the temperature and pressure are high enough to allow flow to take place is the base of the crust. The seismologist can always recognise it by the fact that in the mantle, immediately beneath it, P waves will always travel with a speed of 8·1 km/sec in any part of the earth. Above it, inside the crust, all the geological processes have free reign, and the situation, if not exactly chaotic, is at least complex. In spite of

77

the difficulty in pronunciation, the seismologist generally calls the base of the crust the "Mohorovičić Discontinuity".

The uppermost layers of the crust are composed in the main of sedimentary rocks. We know that these rocks are folded, warped, and tilted to an extraordinary degree; but it is reasonable to expect a more uniform state of affairs in the deeper parts. It has been found, both from studies of local earthquakes, and from special experiments involving artificial explosions, that this is in fact the case; and that it is possible to divide the crust in different places into two main types, one type being found beneath the continents and the other type beneath the oceans.

The continental crust is a two-layered structure, the upper part of which consists of acid crystalline rocks like granite, and the bottom part of more basic rocks like basalt. Underneath the oceans the granitic layer is missing, and in very deep ocean basins the basaltic or, as it is more generally called, the "intermediate" layer becomes very thin. The sedimentary rocks cover crusts of both types to a greater or less extent, but their thickness is very variable.

Our information about the crust comes from a great number of different measurements. The main contribution of the seismologist is derived from the study of near earthquakes and explosions, but he has at least two other ways of obtaining information. The first of these is by studying reflected phases like PP and pP, and the second by studying surface waves.

We saw in Chapter III that the reflected waves come up to the surface of the earth at some part of their journey, and are turned back again. The amount of energy reflected will depend at least in part upon the nature of the crust at the point of reflection. We can use this effect to decide whether the crust is thick or thin in places where near earthquakes do not occur, or where explosion studies are impracticable. Techniques for underwater explosion work, however, are now becoming so reliable, that reflection studies of this kind will soon cease to be so important. They are not precise enough to give a measurement of the crustal thickness, but only to decide to which type the crust belongs. However, the information is valuable in places where no other data exists.

There has recently been a great renewal of interest in surface waves, largely as a result of new theoretical work by the mathematicians; and there are great differences of opinion as to the meaning of some of the results. The aspect of the study which helps us to understand the crust is known as "dispersion". This is not easy to explain, and it will help if we start by clearing up the terms we use when talking about waves. Figure 29 shows an ordinary enough kind of wave. It is of the kind that mathematicians call a "sine wave". Other more com-

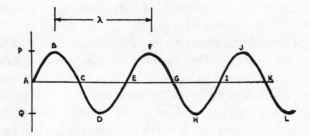

FIG. 29. WAVE MOTION

plicated wave shapes can always be produced by adding together a sufficient number of sine waves of the right kind. B, F, and J are successive crests, and D, H, and L successive troughs. In a simple wave, the distance from B to F or F to J or D to H or H to L is the same. This distance between corresponding points is called the "wave length", and is often abbreviated to the Greek letter lambda ($\lambda$). PQ, the difference in height between the crests and the troughs, is sometimes called the amplitude; but this name is more usually given to PA, the maximum swing in one direction. This is unnecessarily confusing, but fortunately it is generally obvious from the context which of the quantities the writer means. When I use the word "amplitude" I shall mean PA.

If the wave is moving, a certain number of crests will pass a fixed point every second. This number is called the "frequency" of the wave. The frequency, velocity, and wavelength of a wave are connected in a very simple way:

$$\text{Velocity} = \text{Frequency} \times \text{wavelength} \qquad V = N.\lambda$$
$$\text{Frequency} = \text{Velocity} \div \text{wavelength} \qquad N = V/\lambda$$

Since the frequencies in which a seismologist is interested are generally less than one a second, he more often refers to a quantity called the "period". This is the time between the arrival of two successive crests, and is just the reciprocal of the frequency. That means that a frequency of half a cycle a second is a period of two seconds, one of a third of a cycle a second a period of three seconds, and so on.

An earthquake produces waves of a great number of different periods, all mixed up. They start together, but travel at different speeds. The relationship between the speeds and the period of surface waves depends upon the structure of the crustal layers in which they travel. If we look at the tail end, or "coda" of a seismogram, where the L waves are arriving, we will see that the longest periods apparently arrive first, and the shorter and shorter ones come progressively later. It is this process which is called "dispersion". If we know when and where the earthquake took place, we can calculate the speed of travel for waves of each particular period, and plot the result in the form of a graph (Figures 30 and 31). It can be seen that the curves for continental and oceanic crusts have different shapes, and when further theoretical work has been done, it should be possible to make even closer distinctions of crustal type and thickness.

Unlike the results obtained by studying the amplitudes of reflected waves, which refer only to the small region in which the reflection took place, surface wave studies give an average of the conditions over paths many thousands of miles long. The longer the path, the greater the amount of dispersion. The

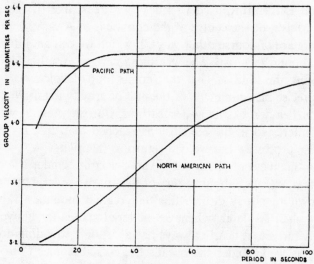

FIG. 30.  DISPERSION OF LOVE WAVES

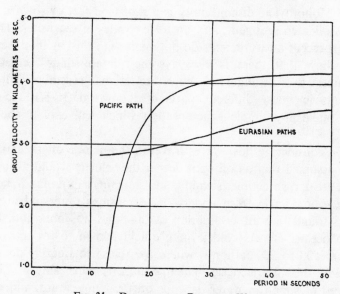

FIG. 31.  DISPERSION OF RAYLEIGH WAVES

81

method is therefore used to study big areas, like the Central Pacific Basin or the centre of the continent of Asia.

There are of course other ways in which we can get information about the crust. The geologist can get useful data by analysing the kind of lava that comes out of volcanoes; and very precise measurements of the pull of gravity tell us whether light or heavy rocks lie underneath us. For the present, we are more interested in the conclusions reached than in the details of these processes, but we will return to them later.

The thickness of the crust is very variable. Under the continents it averages about twenty or twenty-five miles, but it may go down to nearly double this under great mountain ranges. As we shall see later, whenever material stands far above the earth's surface, it nearly always has a "root" extending downwards as well. Under the oceans the crust becomes thin—not more than about five miles or so—and it has been said that in the deepest parts of the oceans, all we can expect to find above the Mohorovičić discontinuity is a thousand feet or so of unconsolidated sediment, and up to five miles of sea water. The most recent measurements do not agree with this, as they seem to show that there is always some "intermediate" crustal material present. Figure 32 shows a selection of crustal measurements in many different parts of the world. It is difficult to make any simple generalisation which will explain them all.

In considering how waves travel in the mantle of the earth, we assumed that as we went deeper the velocity would always get greater, sometimes steadily, and sometimes in jumps. When the sound waves from underwater explosions were studied, it was found that an assumption of this kind was not valid. In the oceans, it gets colder quite quickly down to a depth of from 500 to 700 fathoms, where it is close to freezing-point. Below this the decrease in temperature is much slower. The speed of sound in water depends on the temperature, and on the pressure; and the result of the two acting together is to make it lower at about 700 fathoms than it is either above or

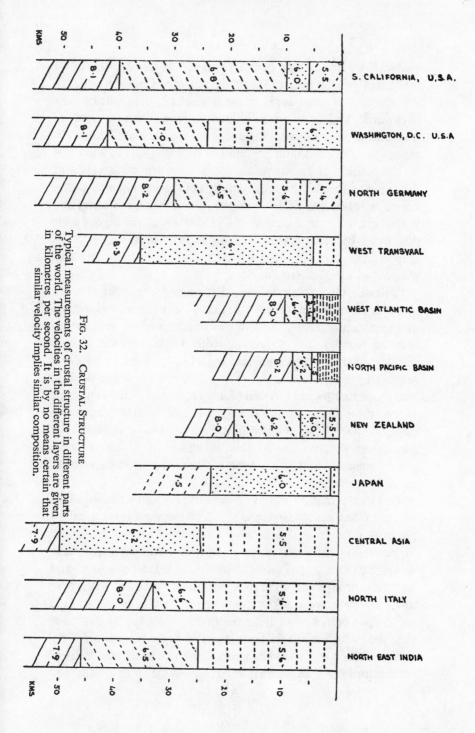

FIG. 32. CRUSTAL STRUCTURE

Typical measurements of crustal structure in different parts of the world. The velocities in the different layers are given in kilometres per second. It is by no means certain that similar velocity implies similar composition.

below. If we fire a small explosive charge at this depth, not all the waves will be able to reach the surface. Unless they leave the source at a great angle to the horizontal, they will be bent backwards and forwards within a narrow channel, and so transmitted to very great distances before they are ultimately absorbed. The explosion of small bombs containing only five or six pounds of explosive has been recorded quite easily at distances of several thousand miles. This sound channel in the ocean is called the SOFAR layer, and it has been suggested that ships, rafts, and aeroplanes in distress could signal their difficulties by firing a small shot in it. In 1948, the U.S. Navy Department proposed to set up receiving stations for this purpose in the Western Pacific.

Professor Gutenberg believes that there is a similar channel in the crust of the earth, and that we shall need to revise some of the conclusions which have been based on the assumption that the velocity always increases with depth. This will change our estimates of the thickness of the crust in continental regions by a few kilometres, but it will not affect the oceanic ones, because they are too thin to include a low-velocity channel. Under the influence of heat and pressure, quartz changes its physical state. The quartz contained in the granite of the continents would undergo this change at a depth of some ten kilometres, and this might produce the drop in velocity needed to produce a channel (Figure 33).

This interpretation would dispose of two long-standing difficulties. When we measure the speed of the waves produced by an explosion at the surface of the earth, we get a slightly higher value than we obtain when we measure earthquake waves. Since they are known to be the same kind of waves, and to travel through the same rock, this is ridiculous. If there were any difference, we would expect the earthquake waves to take the deeper path and to have the higher velocity. By assuming that the earthquake foci lie in the low-velocity channel, Professor Gutenberg is able to explain the observed results quite satisfactorily. At the same time, it is possible to avoid the odd result that P and S waves from some earthquakes did not appear to leave the focus at the same instant.

The mantle of the earth is a much more uniform affair than the crust, and appears to be the same whether we examine it at sea or on land, under plains or ocean deeps, or mountain ranges. It is too deep for us to obtain actual samples, but it probably consists of an ultra-basic rock called dunite, which is mainly olivine. As we go deeper, it becomes denser and more

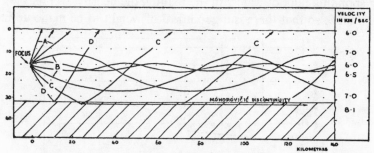

FIG. 33. THE LOW-VELOCITY CHANNEL

The crust of the earth may not be a layered structure, but instead, waves through it may show a gradual change in velocity with depth. In this sketch, the velocity is assumed to increase from 6 km/sec at the surface to 7 km/sec at a depth of 10 km. It then falls again to 6 km/sec at 15 km, and increases once more to about 7 km/sec just above the Mohorovičić discontinuity. With such a structure, waves from an earthquake at the depth of lowest velocity will be confined to a low-velocity channel if they leave the focus in certain directions. A are direct waves to the surface, B the channel rays, C the paths of $P_n$, and D, a ray reflected from the discontinuity.

rigid, and though one or two minor changes occur, its behaviour is free from surprises until we get down to 1800 miles, and reach the boundary of the core.

The speed of waves in the mantle is not, of course, the same at all depths. Just beneath the Mohorovičić discontinuity, as I have explained, it is 8·1 km/sec for P waves, and this increases gradually to about 13·6 km/sec at the boundary of the core. S waves give values of 4·4 km/sec and 7·3 km/sec. At the core, the S waves meet an impenetrable barrier, but P waves can continue, although their speed is once again reduced to 8·1 km/ sec. On the surface of the earth, inability to transmit S waves is regarded as a most important sign that a material is a liquid. Although the core is liquid by this test, it is misleading to think of it as behaving like water. A reliable analogy is difficult to find, and we must be content to think of the material of the core as quite unlike anything we have ever met at the surface of the earth. The core is much denser than the mantle. The density of the whole earth is about $5\frac{1}{2}$, whilst the average of the surface rocks is only about $2\frac{1}{2}$ times as heavy as a corresponding bulk of water. In the mantle, the density averages less than 5, so that there is a good deal of weight to be made up in

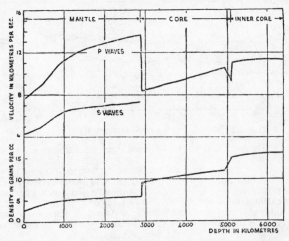

FIG. 34. VARIATION OF VELOCITY AND DENSITY INSIDE THE EARTH

the core, which has a density of 10 to 12 for most of its bulk, and may rise as high as 16 or 17 at the centre. Some geophysicists think that this great density is due to a concentration of heavy metals, like iron and nickel, whilst others think it can be accounted for merely by supposing that the atoms of the materials forming the rest of the earth have been changed under the pressure so that they can be more tightly packed together in the core. This is a question which is not likely to receive a final answer for a long time.

I have already hinted that the core is not a simple structure with the same properties all the way through. In 1936, Miss

Lehmann, the Danish seismologist, examined records of a number of large earthquakes, including the Murchison and Hawkes Bay shocks of 1928 and 1931. It was clear from these records that a P-type wave was arriving at stations which should have been within the shadow zone. This can be explained if there is an inner core, about 1250 km in radius, and of rather greater density than the outer portion. When naming a phase which has travelled through the inner part of the core, we use the letter I if it is a P-type wave, and J if it is an S-type wave.

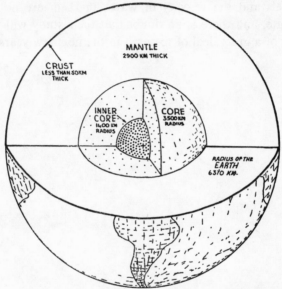

FIG. 35.   THE INTERIOR OF THE EARTH

The phase PKIKP has now been definitely observed, but PKJKP is still doubtful. If it exists, there are reasons to believe that it will not be very strong, so that we can only expect it in big earthquakes. It is probable for other reasons that the inner core is solid, but a record of PKJKP would provide a welcome proof. Figure 34 shows the way in which the density and the velocity of seismic waves change with depth below the earth's surface. We are now in a position to draw a complete picture of the interior of the earth, and this has been done in Figure 35.

It is quite probable that the low-velocity layer in the crust is not the only one to be found inside the earth. There is one in the upper part of the mantle, close to the Mohorovičić discontinuity, Professor Gutenberg thinks; and this accounts for certain peculiarities in the travel times of P and S waves at distances from about 15° to 20°. At the boundary of the core, as we have seen, there is another sharp drop in velocity, which must create still another channel; and there is perhaps a fourth within the core itself. Exact details of the position of these channels and the velocity of waves in them are not easy to calculate, and there is no doubt that their study will form the centre of a great deal of research in the next few years.

# CHAPTER SEVEN

# How Earthquakes Happen

The emperor Justinian prohibited, under penalty of death, certain kinds of sexual offences, together with blasphemy and the practice of swearing by the hair of one's head, on the grounds that such practices notoriously provoked thunderbolts and earthquakes. This seems to me a sound reason. One cannot tolerate conduct which causes earthquakes any more than one can tolerate conduct which leads to riot and disorder.

A. H. CAMPBELL: *Justice and Toleration*

SO far, our study of earthquakes has explained how the earth is put together; but it has done little to explain how earthquakes come to happen at all. Not all tremors originate in the same way, but the great majority of them are what we call "tectonic" earthquakes. The word tectonic comes from the Greek *tekton*, a builder, and implies that the cause of great earthquakes lies in the geological forces responsible for mountain building.

The problem of what happens in the earth near the focus of an earthquake was first solved by H. F. Reid, who studied the effects of the great San Francisco earthquake of 1906, and put forward the "elastic rebound" theory. According to this idea, we should regard earthquakes not as a sudden abnormal happening, but as an effort of the earth to return to normal after it has been slowly strained over a long period of time.

Suppose the rectangle in Figure 36A represents a big tract of country, perhaps 50 or 100 miles across, and that the weakest rocks in it lie along the line AB. Imagine that the dotted lines are very long straight fences built across it. If the block is slowly strained by mountain building forces, or by relative movement between big sections of the crust, it will be deformed so that the fences move to the positions shown in Figure 36B. All the time this is going on—and the process is very slow indeed—elastic energy is being stored up, just as when we wind a spring. Eventually the strain may become so great that the weaker rocks can no longer resist it. Suddenly they break, and the stored energy is released, just as if the coiled spring were suddenly let go. The rocks along the line of weakness (which may be an existing fault) move until they take up a new unstrained position. The movement is greatest near the line, and gets less and less as we go away from it. It is the waves set up by this sudden movement which we call an earthquake. The block diagram (Figure 37) shows the same process in another way. The movement may be horizontal, or vertical, or a combination

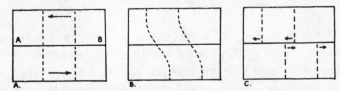

FIG. 36.   ELASTIC REBOUND

After movement has taken place along the fault AB, the country is returned to an unstrained state.

of the two, according to the manner in which the country was originally strained.

The process of fracture and displacement is known to the geologist as "faulting"; but it is not certain that all movements along geological faults are rapid enough to cause earthquakes. In most cases, however, they are, and faults have been called "fossil earthquakes".

Geological faults can be the result of compression, of tension, or of shearing forces, and the displacement of the strata will be different in each case. Figure 38 shows the main types of fault movement, and the names the geologist gives to the resulting faults, and to the parts of a fault. As the last diagram should make clear, transcurrent movement can be associated with a greater or less amount of either "normal" or "reverse" movement at the same time. The name should not be taken as

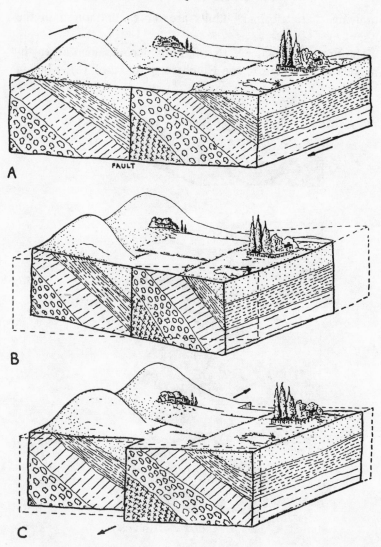

FIG. 37. ELASTIC REBOUND

The elastic strain stored in a block of the earth's crust over a long period of time can be suddenly released by a movement along a fault, causing an earthquake.

implying that "normal" faults are more common than the other types.

The first clear evidence that faulting accompanied an earthquake was obtained in the Cutch earthquake of 1819; but in

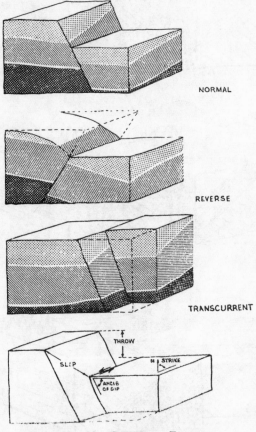

FIG. 38. GEOLOGICAL FAULTING

1927 two Japanese observers reported that the fault trace of the Tango earthquake did not appear until *after* the destruction of their houses. Similar observations had been made in 1891, and this has led some Japanese seismologists to maintain that faulting is the result of earthquakes and not the cause. It should be remembered, however, that a mechanical failure of this kind must develop from some definite point of greatest weakness. This point is the focus of the earthquake, and it is generally buried at some considerable depth. The rate at which the fracture can spread from the focus is less than the speed of seismic waves, and the maximum shaking will in all probability precede the appearance of the dislocation at the surface. If the main energy release did not take place in a limited area, and in a comparatively brief instant of time, a seismogram would present a very complicated appearance, instead of the comparatively orderly sequence of pulses we can observe. Few occidental seismologists would now query the correctness of the elastic rebound theory.

It is only in the larger earthquakes that the fault becomes visible as a rupture of the surface; and superficial slump cracks in the devastated area are usually more obvious to the lay observer, as a study of the plates will show. The vertical movements associated with normal or reverse faulting are often more spectacular than those resulting from transcurrent faults. Geologists have perhaps been led to underestimate the importance of transcurrent movements in consequence.

The Quiches fault in the Peruvian Andes, which appeared as a consequence of the Ancash earthquake of 10th November, 1946, is a remarkable example of a vertical movement. This shock had a magnitude of $7\frac{1}{4}$, and occurred in a particularly inaccessible part of the country. Dr. Enrique Silgado F. and his assistants, who studied the shock, found it necessary to travel for twenty-five days on horse and mule in order to cover the epicentral region, most of which is some 12,000–13,000 ft above sea level. Two parallel fault scarps were found, about 2–3 km. apart, and it appeared that the zone between them had subsided some 10 ft. The largest unbroken length of fault trace extended for 5 km, and showed a maximum vertical displacement of 12 ft. The fault trace vanished where it crossed the very deep Llama Cañon, but reappeared 10 km to the north-west and extended a further 3 km, although the change in level was less marked.

Most New Zealand fault movements have been largely transcurrent, but the White Creek fault, which was responsible for the Murchison earthquake of 1928 is an important exception. It lies in steep bush-clad country, but where it crosses the road a change in level of 14 ft took place. Plate XIX shows river terraces dislocated by the same fault. A closer examination of the picture will reveal that the bush-clad hill in the middle distance has been severed, and that the trace continues to the distant skyline.

Transcurrent movement with little or no vertical component often leaves the ground surface apparently undisturbed, particularly in level country. Nevertheless, it can produce some odd effects, such as the successive displacement of rows of trees in a Californian orchard seen in Plate XVII. This occurred in the Imperial Valley earthquake of September 1940. A New Zealand example appeared in the Hawkes Bay earthquake of 1931, and the road, fence, and railway near Paki Paki, seen in Plate XVIII show a horizontal offset of some 6 ft. Alexander McKay's report on the Cheviot earthquake of 1901, which is discussed in Chapter XII, contains the picture of a fence offset by 9 ft in the earthquakes of September 1888, and this has been reproduced in several well-known geological text-books.

Although fault movements may be inconspicuous, they extend to a depth at least as great as that of the focus. In the Peruvian example given, this was estimated as 30–40 km. The biggest visible displacement known to have resulted from a single shock (and possibly some associated aftershocks) was an uplift of 47 ft in the Yakutat Bay region of Alaska, following the shocks of September 1899.

By matching the sequence of rocks on opposite sides of a fault, the geologist can tell us how much it has moved, even if it was formed long before man was living on the earth. The biggest displacements which take place in a single earthquake amount to about ten or perhaps twenty feet; but geologists have found faulting which shows that enormous movements totalling many miles have taken place. The New Zealand geologist, Dr. Wellman, considers that the great Alpine fault on the western side of the Southern Alps may involve a displacement of two or three hundred miles, so that rocks which are now in Nelson once were continuous with similar rocks in Otago. Of course, this was not the result of a single enormous earthquake. The shearing forces which act upon New Zealand must have been exerted in the same direction for a very long time, so that successive earthquake movements of a few inches or a few feet have added up to the present enormous total. Recently evidence has been gathered by both geologists and geophysicists suggesting that around the Pacific these horizontal transcurrent movements are by far the most common type.

There is an upper and a lower limit to the size of an earthquake. Once the strength of the rocks is reached, faulting must take place and release the accumulated strain. The stronger the rocks are, the bigger an earthquake can be. In Chapter I we considered ways of estimating the felt strength of a shock. Whilst the maximum felt strength gives us some idea of the energy released, we also need to know the depth of focus, and whether the strongest felt report was really near the epicentre. The epicentre might for instance, have been at sea where there was nobody to feel it. The figure we use to describe the total energy of the shock is called the Magnitude. The difference between the energies given on the magnitude scale, and the felt intensities on the modified Mercalli or Rossi-Forel scales is very important. A shock can have as many intensities as there are observers, but it has only one magnitude. When newspapers print information about earthquakes, their reporters very often get these things badly mixed, with the results that their reports annoy the people that know the difference, and confuse the ones who do not.

Earthquake magnitudes are worked out from seismograph records. The scale was first devised by Professor Richter for Californian earthquakes, and depends upon the maximum recorded amplitude shown on a standard type of seismograph.

Records from other types have to be reduced to the standard scale by special calculations. The standard instrument chosen was the Wood-Anderson torsion seismometer, with a period of 0·8 sec, critical damping, and a magnification of 2800. Since the New Zealand network included a number of these instruments, the scale was immediately adopted here; but even after more than ten years the public are less familiar with it than with the old intensity scales.

The upper limit of magnitude, set by the strength of the rock, is round about 8·6. Any earthquake of magnitude 8 or more is a very great one indeed. The famous Lisbon earthquake of 1755, the California earthquake in 1906, and the Assam earthquake of 1950 all had magnitude of more than 8. Although the Wellington earthquake of 1855 was probably nearly as big as this, the Hawkes Bay shock in 1931, which is the biggest New Zealand earthquake since we have had seismographs, only reached 7¾. Anything much above 7 is a major disaster, and 5 is enough to cause considerable damage to chimneys and plaster, and to goods stacked up in window displays. Many of the small felt shocks in New Zealand have a magnitude about 3½, but below magnitude 2 it is unlikely that the shock will be reported felt at all.

The smallest possible shock needs enough energy to unlock a fault and set it moving. This quantity of energy is not very easy to determine, but a value not far from magnitude 0 seems likely. Magnitude 0 is just a number on a scale. It doesn't mean that there would be no energy in a shock of that size, any more than a thermometer reading of 0°C implies that there is no heat left in the bulb. Just as we have minus temperatures to indicate very small amounts of heat, we can have minus magnitudes to represent very small amounts of earthquake energy. Professor Bullen has calculated the volume of the region in which the rocks would have to be strained to produce the largest earthquakes. If they were all very nearly at breaking point, it would be about that of a sphere 25 miles in radius.

After a large earthquake, there are generally a great number

Plate XIII

VERTICAL FAULTING. A fault scarp 12 ft. high at Quiches, in the Peruvian Andes, which appeared in the Ancash earthquake of November 10, 1946. Further views of the same fault are seen in Plates XV and XVI.

Plate XIV

VERTICAL FAULTING. The White Creek Fault, responsible for the Murchison earthquake in 1928, caused this 14 ft. high barrier across a road.

Plate XV and Plate XVI

**VERTICAL FAULTING.** Two further pictures of the Quiches fault. Note that the scarp is very little affected by the changes in surface topography.

Plate XVII
TRANSCURRENT FAULTING. This aerial photograph of a Californian orange grove shows displacement of the rows of trees by faulting during the Imperial Valley earthquake in September 1940. *'Photo David Scherman—By courtesy of Life Magazine'*

Plate XVIII
TRANSCURRENT FAULTING. A six foot horizontal movement at Paki Paki, south of Hastings, N.Z. in the 1931 Hawkes Bay earthquake. The offset of the fence is clearly visible, but a small surface rent like this would be rapidly obliterated.

Plate XIX

WHITE CREEK FAULT. Another view of part of the fault responsible for the Murchison earthquake of 1928. The most obvious effect is the displacement of the river terraces, but the trace continues through the bush-covered hill in the background.

Plate XX

SUPERFICIAL SLUMPING. Bridge approaches, which consist largely of filled material, are particularly liable to develop spectacular cracks. The bridge itself has collapsed as a result of relative movement of piers and abutments. Murchison, 1928.

of smaller ones from almost the same origin. The simple elastic rebound theory does not make it at all clear why these after-shocks should occur. If the main shock releases the energy stored in the strained country, why doesn't the fault go on moving until all the strain is gone? The accumulation of enough energy to unlock the fault again after it has once stopped moving should take considerable time; yet the early aftershocks are sometimes almost as big as the main shock itself. It had often been suggested that the main shock might re-distribute the remaining stresses in the area, so as to make energy available which could not be released by the first shock itself, and that the fault, once it had been unlocked, would probably move more easily if it hadn't had time to cement up again. A few years ago, Dr. Hugo Benioff, who designed the seismograph already described, made a study of the magnitude of these small shocks and their relation in time to the main shock, and has been able to put forward a much more convincing explanation. In order to understand it, we must first make a study of what happens to materials when we compress them.

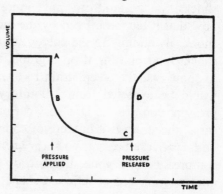

FIG. 39. ELASTIC CREEP

When pressure is applied to a rock sample, part of the compression occurs immediately, but contraction continues to take place for a long time afterwards at a very slow rate. On releasing the pressure, part of the contraction is immediately recovered, but the rest is only very slowly released during a period of "elastic afterworking".

Suppose we have a sample of rock in our laboratory, which can be squashed in a special hydraulic press, and some means of measuring just how much we squash it. If we apply the pressure, and leave it for a long time, measuring the change in bulk from time to time, we will get results which can be plotted on a graph like Figure 39. When the pressure is first applied, at A, the rock will immediately contract to a smaller bulk, B. If we continue to exert the same pressure, it will continue to contract for a long time afterwards, but at an ever decreasing rate. When the point C is reached, we release the pressure again. The rock recovers at once, but it does not come right back to its original size. It comes back quickly to D, so that CD represents the same amount of change as AB, and then takes its time about the rest of the recovery. This recovery process is known as "elastic afterworking" or "creep strain recovery", and Benioff considers that it is responsible for aftershocks.

Elastic rebound can only release the stored energy corresponding to CD; this causes the main earthquake. But stress across the fault is immediately set up again as the elastic afterworking takes place. This energy is released in small aftershocks, for the fault can move more easily and extend further now that it has been freed by the movement causing the main shock. By adding up the energy stored in a sequence of aftershocks, and plotting it on a graph, Dr. Benioff has been able to show that the creep strain recovers in exactly the way that would be expected from laboratory studies of the effect of pressure upon rocks. One very curious thing happens. In most cases, the strain is a mixture of compression and shear. When both types are present, no shear energy is released until all the compression has gone. Because of this, the graph is broken into two portions of different shape; and the shapes are those laboratory experiment has led us to expect. Figure 40 shows the graph for the sequence of aftershocks which followed the Cheviot earthquake of 10th January, 1951.

In describing the mechanism of an earthquake, we began by assuming that certain forces were at work in the crust of the earth. That this is a justifiable assumption is evident from the folding, faulting, and uplift of rocks which we can see all around us; but we have still to discuss the origin of the forces themselves.

At the present time, there is no general agreement about the most probable way in which the earth was formed. Some astronomers think that it may at one time have been part of the material of the sun, and was ejected from it by an eruption, or torn from it by the gravitational pull of some passing star. Others believe that it could have been formed of matter gathered from space by the sun's own attraction, and concentrated around small nuclei to form the planets. This leaves us without a clear answer to two questions—was it hot or cold in the first place, and what proportions of the different elements did it

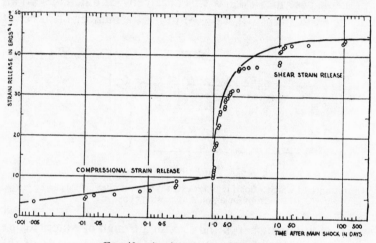

FIG. 40.   AN AFTERSHOCK SEQUENCE

This graph shows the strain released in the aftershocks which followed the Cheviot earthquake of 1951, Jan. 10.

originally contain? The outer parts of the earth contain a considerable amount of radio-active material; and it is certain that if the earth was not hot when it was originally formed, it must rapidly have become so when these materials were concentrated together in a single body.

This early heating up in a great degree explains the difference in composition between the rocks of the continents and those of the oceans. Since that time, cooling has been taking place. Naturally, the outer layers of the earth cool more rapidly than the interior; and as they cool, they tend not only to solidify,

99

but to contract. The earth inside the jacket continues to cool and shrink, and as a result, great compressional forces are set up in the crust. The process of cooling must also have set up great convection currents in the mantle, and these may still continue. Convection currents of this kind would assist in the concentration of the continental material and the formation of the great mountain ranges at the continental margins.

Another important source of crustal forces results from the operation of what is known as the "principle of isostasy". This principle describes a delicate balance between different sections of the earth's crust. If we were to float a number of pieces of

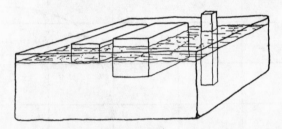

FIG. 41. THE PRINCIPLE OF ISOSTASY

The distance to which a floating block extends beneath the surface can be judged from the amount appearing above it.

wood of different shapes and sizes in a trough of water (Figure 41), we would find, provided that they were all made of the same kind of wood, that a big block which sticks a long way out of the water also goes a long way underneath. Similarly, a a thin plank which doesn't stick up much doesn't go down very far beneath the water either. Now, the material which makes up the continents is resting upon the denser material of the mantle in a way that is not very different from floating. If every bit of the continent was able to find its own level independently, we would expect the bottom of the crust to lie very much deeper under the mountain ranges than it does under the plains, and on the average, this is just what happens. We can get proof of this in several ways, one of which is from earthquake waves which have to pass underneath one of the big mountain ranges.

Mountain roots also have an effect upon the pull of gravity. Imagine that we hang up a plumb-bob somewhere in the middle of a great continental plain (Figure 42). Both the light material of the mantle and the heavier material of the crust stretch away evenly in all directions, and the pull of gravity makes the plumb-bob hang straight down. If we could place a mountain range on top of the plain, without altering anything else, there would be more material to one side of the bob than the other, and the great mass of the mountain would pull the bob a little in its direction. When measurements are made near mountain ranges, it is found that this does not take place. The explanation is that under a real mountain, there is a root sticking down into the mantle which drives out just enough of the heavy material

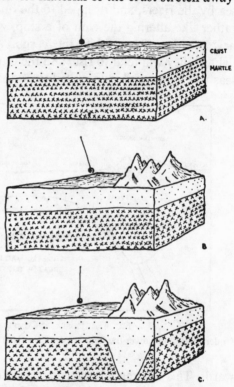

CRUST
MANTLE

A.

B.

C.

FIG. 42. DEFLECTION OF THE PLUMB-LINE

A. Plain, fully compensated, line vertical.
B. Uncompensated mountain, line deflected.
C. Mountain compensated by root, line vertical.

and replaces it with light to leave the same total mass on all sides of the pendulum. The bob therefore hangs straight down once more.

This floating of the continents is called "isostasy", and regions in which the plumb-bob will hang vertical and there is no tendency for the land either to rise or to sink are called

101

"compensated" (Figure 43). Large areas of the earth seem to be very nearly compensated, but they are unlikely to remain so for ever. In Chapter 5 we saw how mountain ranges are continually being eroded away, and their rocks transported to the sea by the rivers, and dropped to the bottom. This has a result rather like altering the trim of a ship, which has to take up a new position if you shift the cargo. As the mountains get lighter, they will tend to rise, and the crust beneath the shallow seas where material is deposited tends to become warped down-

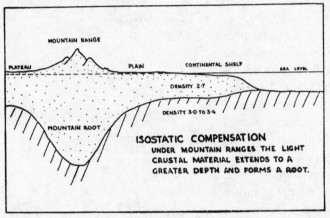

FIG. 43. ISOSTATIC COMPENSATION

Under mountain ranges the light crustal material extends to a greater depth and forms a root.

wards. This differential tendency naturally sets up great strains in the country between. Departures from the compensated conditions are known as "isostatic anomalies", and they can be investigated by measuring local changes in gravity with the help of portable instruments called gravimeters. Before the readings of these instruments can be interpreted, however, complicated allowances have to be made for the local configuration of the country, the height above sea level, and any departure from normal density in the rocks due to purely local geological features.

In addition to isostatic readjustment, there may be another process tending to move the continents about. According to

Wegener's theory of continental drift, when continent and ocean were first formed, there was only one of each. At a later stage of history, the continent split up into pieces which drifted apart until they reached the position of the continental masses we see today. The bulge of South America, for example, is supposed to have fitted into the curve of Africa. By no means all geologists and geophysicists agree that this could have happened, but there is a large amount of evidence in favour of something of the kind. If continental drift is still occurring, it is another possible source of earthquake-causing stresses.

Whilst the details of some of these geological processes are still open to question, the main outline of the story is clear. Strains can originate in the earth's crust as a result of a large number of different causes. When that strain is released by new faulting, or by sudden movement on an existing fault, an earthquake is the result.

Many attempts have been made to determine the direction of the strains acting in different parts of the world. We cannot claim to understand the crust until we know both what it is made of, and what forces act upon it. One of the most promising ways of investigating crustal forces is to study the direction in which rocks on the two sides of a fault have been displaced. This can be done by studying the direc-tion of the first

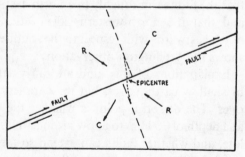

FIG. 44.   DIRECTION OF THE INITIAL IMPULSE
Compressions and rarefactions are distributed in quadrants, depending on the orientation of the fault and the direction in which the movement takes place.

movement recorded by a seismograph, as well as by examin-ing the rocks themselves.

Figure 44 shows a fault with its plane perpendicular to the paper, and the forces in the region are supposed to

103

tend to make the rocks on the upper side of it move to the right. All the seismograph stations in the quadrants marked C will find that the first ground movement is towards them, and away from the epicentre; whilst those in the quadrants marked R will record movements away from the station, and towards the epicentre. The first kind of movement is called a compression, and the second a rarefaction. A team of scientists in Canada is examining big earthquakes in all parts of the world to try to find out which way the faults are moving. This is not quite as simple as it might seem, because the fact that the earth is a sphere modifies the simple theory, and at distant stations it is complicated by the reflection or refraction of the simple P wave.

If we study a small area, in which most of the faults can be assumed to run parallel, and to move in the same direction, the results from a single seismograph station can be used to obtain the information. With only a single component seismograph, there are six regions in which the first movement changes direction alternately. A New Zealand study of this kind shows that the faults run roughly in a north-east-south-west direction, and that the north-western side of the fault tends to move north-eastwards with respect to the south-eastern side. Figure 45 shows the Wellington observations.

Explanations of this kind are fairly satisfactory for normal or shallow earthquakes, but they are less satisfactory for deep ones. The doubtful point is whether the earth is rigid enough at a depth of 700 km to allow ordinary elastic strains to accumulate, and whether faults can extend so far beneath the crust. If they cannot do so, then another explanation must be found for deep focus earthquakes. One such explanation is that the cooling of the earth sets up convection currents in the mantle, and that because of a different rate of heat flow through the floors of the oceans and through the continents, there is a concentration of the resultant stresses at their margins. This system can extend to a very great depth, but below 700 km the material can flow so readily that the strain can be relieved gradually, instead of being stored and released as earthquakes. Unfortunately, recent measurements indicate that at present this difference in heat flow is very small. Two important facts must be considered in any discussion of the cause of deep-focus

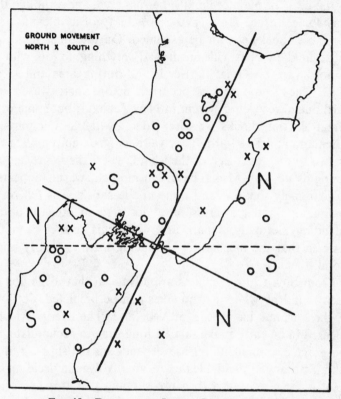

FIG. 45. DIRECTION OF INITIAL GROUND MOVEMENT

This map distinguishes between epicentres from which the first impulse recorded at Wellington moved to the north, and those from which the movement was to the south. Note the tendency to distribution in alternate sectors.

earthquakes—they are not followed by aftershock sequences; and the very largest deep-focus shocks are smaller than the biggest shallow ones. Perhaps the true answer to the problem lies in a combination of the faulting and convection hypotheses.

From May to December 1922 the small township of Taupo

in the centre of the North Island experienced a great number of moderately severe earthquakes, and although the larger ones did some minor damage, there was no definite main shock. Such an occurrence is called an earthquake swarm. Taupo is in the heart of New Zealand's thermal area, and although there was some surface faulting, the possibility of a volcanic origin for these shocks cannot be excluded. On the other hand, it is most unlikely that vulcanism had anything to do with the minor swarm at Great Barrier Island during June and July of 1953. The Taupo shocks occurred before there was a local earthquake recording system in New Zealand; but some of the Great Barrier shocks were recorded by the seismographs at Auckland and Karapiro. They were assigned epicentres a mile or two to the north-east of the island, where they were felt with strengths up to MM 4. The origin of such swarms appears to be extremely shallow, and none of the shocks was felt on the mainland. Similar swarms have occurred in other countries, including Germany, Japan, and California, but it cannot be claimed that the mechanism producing them is clearly understood.

From time to time, claims are advanced that a method has been found by which earthquakes can be predicted. So far all of these claims have been proved false. The energy which is released in an earthquake takes a long time to accumulate, and the exact instant of its release depends on the slipping of the fault. So many incalculable factors are involved in deciding how great a force is needed to cause slipping that this line of approach is ruled out at once. We would need to know how far the fault extended beneath the ground, and the strength of all the rocks on either side of the fault face, how rough the fault surface is, and how much force is pressing the faces together.

It is widely believed that the approach of a large shock is heralded by a sharp increase in the number of small ones. This is the exception rather than the rule, unless the shocks are of volcanic origin. At the most, one or two foreshocks are likely, and there is no way of distinguishing them from normal minor

106

activity. Japanese workers have found some evidence of abnormal ground tilting before large earthquakes, but this can also result from meteorological causes, and as yet there is nothing definite enough known to serve as the basis of a useful forecast. Nevertheless, there has recently been renewed interest in this branch of study.

The attempts at prediction which merit most scientific discussion are those based on the idea that slipping of a fault can be initiated by some secondary trigger force, which acts as a "last straw" and sets it moving. A great deal of attention has been paid to possible triggers. Tidal loading, and a variety of meteorological factors seem to be the most reasonable ones so far to be studied. Planetary attractions are so much smaller than other variable forces at work that they can have no appreciable effect. The best that can be claimed at present is that in certain areas there seems to be a slightly greater tendency for earthquakes to happen when the barometer is rising than when it is falling; or the other way round according to the district. This is naturally useless for the purposes of prediction; and it is equally far removed from the popular notions of "earthquake weather", which have no basis in fact.

"Hope ushers in a revolution as earthquakes are preceded by bright weather", wrote Carlyle in his *French Revolution*. With this seismological pronouncement, the Japanese are not in agreement. They consider that earthquake weather is hot and humid; but when Omori examined the weather conditions for eighteen major earthquakes spread over 530 years, he found that twelve happened on fine days, two on cloudy days, and four on rainy days. The only safe conclusion to be drawn from this concerns the nature of the Japanese climate.

In New Zealand, R. C. Hayes has examined the position without obtaining any significant results. If there is any connection between our earthquakes and our weather, we should expect it to be much less noticeable in the case of the many epicentres lying under the sea, since the daily pressure changes on the sea bottom which result from the rising and falling of the tides are ten times larger than the greatest changes in air pressure. The most striking effect which he found was a marked tendency for the aftershocks of the Cook Strait earthquake in early 1950 to occur when the tide was falling, and the barometer was lower than normal.

In the Himalayas, the frequency of small earth tremors is found to be related to flood conditions in the rivers, a high rate of change of flood intensity being particularly likely to trigger off minor swarms.

Although the possibility of trigger action remains an interesting field for investigation, its practical value as a method of forecasting is likely to remain small. The utility of earthquake prediction, indeed, is open to question. It would be necessary to have a very accurate idea of the position, the time, and the intensity of the coming shock before evacuation or some similar precaution would be practicable. There is little consolation in knowing beforehand that your house is about to fall down, and it is probably wiser to turn our ingenuity and our labours to framing sound building codes and devising better methods of construction.

The position has been admirably summed up by the Japanese seismologist Suyehiro in a lecture to American engineers. It was no use, he explained, worrying about the trigger being pulled when it was most likely the gun was not loaded. If the charge in the earthquake gun is large enough, it will go off whether the trigger is pulled or not.

# CHAPTER EIGHT

# Where Earthquakes Happen

... the smoke and stir of this dim spot
Which men call Earth.
                              MILTON: *Comus*

NEW ZEALAND is often described as "an earthquake
country". The phrase implies that we have more earthquakes than other parts of the world, but even in New Zealand
there are differences in the number of shocks felt in the different
towns and cities. In this chapter, we will see just where earthquakes are most likely to happen.

The liability of a district to earthquake is called its "seismicity", and there are a number of different ways of assessing
it. Which method is the most helpful will depend on the use
to which the information is to be put. One obvious way to
measure seismicity is to count the number of epicentres in a
region, and to consider their magnitude or felt intensity. This
has a great practical disadvantage. A town some distance outside the region in which the shocks are centred can still be
close enough to feel them, and perhaps even close enough to
be damaged by the larger ones. This is true of the city of Auckland. No epicentres have been located in the region west of
the Firth of Thames, and north of the mouth of the Waikato
River; but a large earthquake in the Hauraki Gulf or on the
Coromandel Peninsula could have serious consequences in
Auckland. This is one of the reasons why the seismologist needs
felt reports to supplement the readings of his instruments.

Before we look at local conditions, let us consider the earth
as a whole. Most published maps which try to indicate the
earthquake belts are misleading, as they do not take into
account the magnitude of the shocks. This has the effect of

109

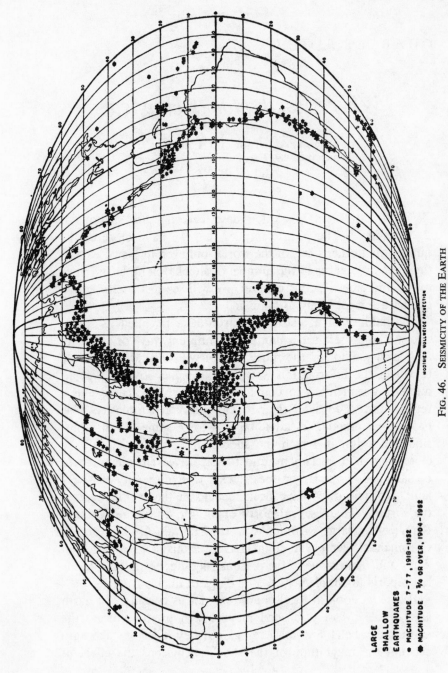

FIG. 46.  SEISMICITY OF THE EARTH

Epicentres of large shallow shocks (from Gutenberg and Richter).

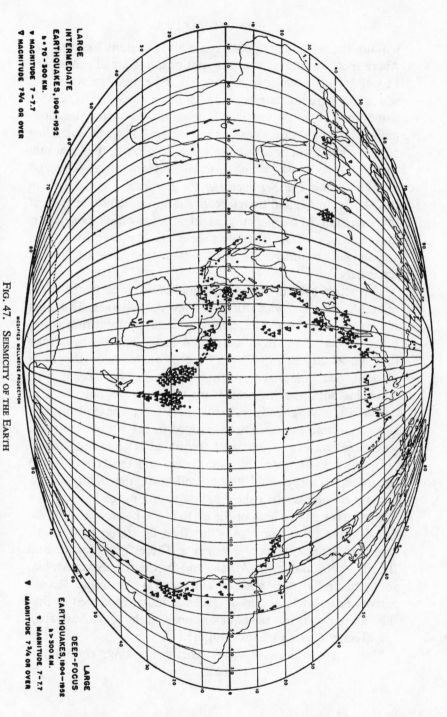

**LARGE
INTERMEDIATE
EARTHQUAKES, 1904—1952**

h=70-300 KM.

▽ MAGNITUDE 7 - 7.7

▽ MAGNITUDE 7¾ OR OVER

**LARGE
DEEP-FOCUS
EARTHQUAKES, 1904—1952**

h > 300 KM.

▼ MAGNITUDE 7 - 7.7

▼ MAGNITUDE 7¾ OR OVER

FIG. 47.  SEISMICITY OF THE EARTH

Epicentres of large deep and intermediate shocks (from Gutenberg and Richter).

making the seismicity appear too high in regions like Europe, where there are many recording stations, and small shocks can be well located; whilst in regions like Tibet and the Antarctic, where there are no stations, only the large shocks are observed. Conditions in the Antarctic will be improved during the International Geophysical Year, when several nations, including New Zealand, will be setting up scientific bases in the far south. Figures 46 and 47, which are taken from Gutenberg and Richter's book *The Seismicity of the Earth* do not suffer from this shortcoming, and therefore give a fairer picture, in spite of the omission of very many small shocks whose position is known. The ordinary shallow shocks and the deep-focus ones are shown on different maps so that they may be studied separately.

The active belts in which earthquakes occur lie at the edges of stable blocks in which there are few earthquakes. This does not mean that the stable regions are entirely free from them, but only that they are infrequent. A large shallow shock may take place almost anywhere. Of the active belts, the most obvious one completely surrounds the Pacific Ocean. This coincides with the important crustal structure boundary to which we have already referred, and it is consequently no surprise to find the epicentres grouped in this way at the place where the crustal stresses are concentrated. The second important belt runs through the East Indies and the Himalayas to the Mediterranean, and loses itself near the Azores. This activity closely parallels the great mountain ranges.

The largest stable area of the earth is the basin of the Pacific Ocean; but there are also a number of stable land areas, generally in the interior of continents. These are in Canada and Brazil, in the Baltic, in Africa, and in Central Asia, Arabia, southern India, and western and central Australia. Recent activity near Adelaide and in Queensland has reminded us that the immunity from earthquakes boasted by our Australian neighbours is by no means absolute.

The active regions are not, strictly speaking, continuous.

They are associated with a variety of large but separate geological structures; but the activity related to neighbouring features tends to merge into a single picture. Careful study of the maps will explain this more clearly than words can do.

Shallow and deep-focus activity is not exactly superimposed, but as a rule, there is some kind of regular arrangement in depth. This is most clearly brought out in the Pacific formations known to the structural geologist as "island arcs". Beginning on the convex side of the arc, there is a regular sequence of geophysical features. First comes a deep oceanic trench, with a narrow but active belt of shallow earthquakes close to its inside edge. Gravity is lower than normal in this region, and there may be a few small islands where the ocean bottom again rises in a ridge. Beyond this, gravity becomes normal, and then greater than normal above a region in which the earthquakes get deeper, perhaps 50–100 km. Then come the main islands of the arc, generally formed in the Cretaceous or the Tertiary period. They often have active volcanoes. Behind this is an older or secondary arc, with extinct or nearly extinct volcanoes; and earthquakes at about 200 km. Finally there is the really deep earthquake activity at up to nearly 700 km (Figure 48). The very deep shocks seem to occur only around the Pacific. In other parts of the world, about 300 km is a more usual limit, although there was recently a striking exception beneath North Africa, south of Spain. The deepest shocks of all occur in the Tonga-Kermadec region, just to the north-east of New Zealand, so that deep-focus earthquakes have a special interest to us.

The New Zealand reader will naturally want to know the seismicity of his own country in rather more detail; and it will serve as a suitable example of a more limited area for readers elsewhere. Most of New Zealand, with the exception of the North Auckland peninsula, lies within the mobile belt encircling the Pacific, and major earthquakes are to be expected. Both Wellington and Christchurch have experienced more than one destructive shock since the beginning of European settlement; and Auckland and Dunedin have had a few damaging ones to remind them that they are not outside the possible danger area. The pattern of present activity largely confirms the one deduced by the geologists from their mapping of Recent

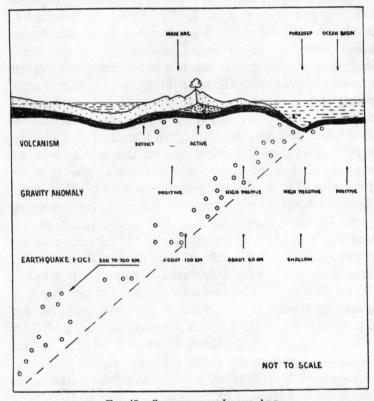

FIG. 48.    SECTION OF AN ISLAND ARC

faults, but the epicentres tend to lie near the faults rather than accurately upon them. This appears to be usual everywhere. It seems that we must leave the large faults for the large earthquakes, and assign the minor activity to comparatively minor fractures which give little surface evidence of their existence.

The pattern of deep-focus activity is particularly interesting, as it throws some light upon the overall geological structure of the country, and upon its relationship with the great ocean deep stretching between Tonga and the Kermadecs. The shock at a depth of 570 km which took place in North Taranaki seems to be an isolated occurrence; but it lies on the correct side of the other activity to conform with the general pattern. Otherwise, the maximum depth is less than 400 km. Now that we know that these extra deep shocks exist, it may be possible to locate more of them. The rest of the activity lies within a kind of three-sided wedge, with the apex in Marlborough or North Canterbury and the base along the shore of the Bay of Plenty. Under the Bay of Plenty, the shocks lie at depths down to about 370 km; under Marlborough they are at less than 100 km. In general, the deeper shocks lie slightly to the west of the shallower ones. Figure 49 shows the country cut into a series of slices, and should clarify the arrangement in depth of the earthquake foci.

A very useful index of the liability of a place to earthquake damage can be obtained by considering its relationship to the biggest shocks which have been recorded in the past, provided that the records cover a long enough period of time. Figure 50 shows the epicentres of all the destructive earthquakes reported in New Zealand. The records go back to about 1835, but in earlier times the country was very sparsely populated, and the felt reports alone may leave an uncertainty of twenty miles or so in the true position. Systematic felt reports have been kept since about 1865, but the first New Zealand seismograph was not erected until 1904.

I have often been asked to compare the seismicity of New Zealand with that of Japan and California, two regions which the public associates with big earthquakes. The question is largely answered by the world epicentre maps. Japan has a similar type of activity to that in New Zealand. Both shallow and deep-focus earthquakes are present, and the largest shocks reach magnitude 8. Big shocks of this kind are more frequent in Japan than in New Zealand, and the destructive effects are increased by the occurrence of *tsunami*, or seismic sea waves. These are discussed in Chapter 10. California also has large earthquakes, the San Francisco shock of 1906 being very well

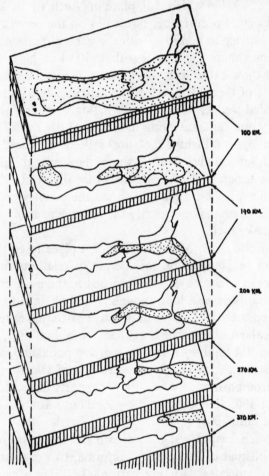

FIG. 49. DISTRIBUTION IN DEPTH OF NEW ZEALAND EARTHQUAKES

known, but there is no deep-focus activity. The number of shocks is not very different from that in New Zealand.

Listing the destructive earthquakes in the different countries may give some basis for a comparison of the seismicity in

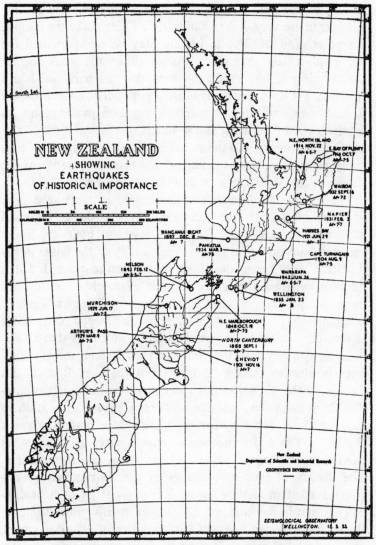

FIG. 50.   DESTRUCTIVE EARTHQUAKES IN NEW ZEALAND

Early epicentres have been deduced from felt data, and may be 20 miles or more in error.

117

human terms, but its scientific value is limited. The regions considered are very different in size, and places like the oceans, the poles, and the Pacific islands may be unrepresented for the good reason that there are no observations. A further shortcoming results from the fact that in parts of South America, for instance, many closely populated towns are built of mud brick, and suffer disproportionate damage and casualties from shocks of quite moderate intensity. The relation of this kind of "seismicity" to the strength of the buildings also leads many people to over-estimate the number and severity of the shocks in the Mediterranean and the Middle East.

The very practically minded man sometimes demands a more personal answer to the question "Where do earthquakes happen?" "I don't want," he will say, "to build my house across a fault line. Can you give me a map of the faults in my district?" Sometimes these faults have been mapped; but it is doubtful whether the information is of much value for this particular purpose. The whole of a country like New Zealand is intensively faulted, but in many cases, the age of the fault is very difficult to determine. The geologist knows that a fault must be younger than the youngest rock it cuts, and is consequently able to classify a number of them as Recent. But Recent, to the geologist, may mean any time in the last twenty-five thousand years, and the fault may have no intention of moving again. The only certain proof that a fault is active is the knowledge that someone has seen it move. In this case, it cannot move again until a sufficient strain has accumulated. The history of past earthquakes in the district may give a rough indication of how long this is likely to be. A final difficulty is that in flat land, on which men usually prefer to build, there may be a good deal of surface cover of old river gravel, soil, and similar material hiding the fault structure underneath.

There seems to be a widespread idea that certain people live "on the earthquake line", where shocks are more strongly felt than they are in other neighbouring places. The announcement is often made with a certain pride, and as far as I can gather, the "line" is pictured as a kind of wriggly snake stretching its erratic and sinister length across the countryside. Many towns have localities which are reputed to lie on it. In Wellington, at least, the places I have heard so described are in the older parts of the city, where the buildings are undoubtedly more shaky. Certainly, not all parts of a city will feel an earthquake with equal intensity, but the reasons are related to the differences in foundation, and the "earthquake line" is a pure fiction.

CHAPTER NINE

# Earthquakes and Volcanoes

BANQUO: The earth hath bubbles, as the water has,
And these are of them.
SHAKESPEARE: *Macbeth*

MANY people associate earthquakes and volcanoes. In New Zealand, we have plenty of both; but the earthquakes do not happen just because there are volcanoes in the Tongariro National Park, and hot springs at Whakarewarewa. Volcanoes and earthquakes are different results of the geological structure of the country.

When we discussed the interior of the earth, we saw that it could not be liquid near the surface on account of the enormous pressure exerted by the rocks of the crust, which effectively keeps it from melting. The crust, however, is not everywhere of the same thickness, and is not everywhere in one piece. It is faulted into separate blocks, and contains layers of different materials. Consequently there are some regions in which it is mechanically weak. The molten material deep in the earth, known as "magma", can force its way up through cracks and along lines of weakness. Usually it does this by a comparatively unspectacular process known as "intrusion". The magma, having forced itself a certain distance through the crack, or along the interface between strata, solidifies to form a "sill" or "dyke" of igneous rock. If the conditions are suitable, and the magma behaves in a less controlled manner, a volcano may result.

A volcano starts as a vent through which escaping gases and ash can reach the surface. Scoria, pumice, ash, and so on piles up around the vent, and usually builds up the typical cone-shaped mountain. The rate of growth of the cone is often

120

extremely rapid. At Paricutín, in Mexico, a few years ago, an old vent in a farmer's paddock became active. There was comparatively little warning, but after a day or two, great quantities of ash were being thrown out, and the cone had started to grow. Within the next two or three years it attained a height of several thousand feet, and was still erupting. This is one of the few cases in which it has been possible to study a volcano right from the instant of its birth. If magma reaches the surface in liquid form, it may flow from the crater as lava. The temperature of lava is, as a rule, not much more than about 1200° C. This is only just sufficient to keep it molten, and it soon cools and solidifies, helping to build up the cone still further.

Volcanoes are classified according to the manner in which they habitually erupt; but since they often change their habits in the course of time, the classification is of limited use. The quietest type is the Hawaiian volcanoes, which seldom explode violently, preferring to pour out quantities of a very liquid basaltic lava, and building up mounds of scoria close to their vents. In the next type, like Stromboli, the lava is still basaltic in composition, but much less liquid, and is often thrown up in gas fountains and small explosions. The Vulcanian type, named after the original Vulcano in the Lipari Islands off the coast of Italy, has an even stiffer type of lava, composed of more acid rock which tends to harden inside the crater. Volcanoes of this type often send up great clouds of fine ash in a "cauliflower" cloud. The wind disperses this material over very wide areas, and there are thick deposits of ash from ancient eruptions of this type all over the Tongariro-Taupo region. The last type of volcano, the Peléean, is named after Mont Pelée in Martinique, the scene of a disastrous eruption which destroyed the town of St. Pierre in 1902. These volcanoes send out what are called *nuées ardentes*—dense clouds of gases and incandescent material which tumble over the edge of the crater and roll swiftly down the slope. The lava in these volcanoes is so stiff that it can form an apparently solid plug in the mouth of the vent. Sometimes the pressure underneath forces the plug high into the air to form a "spine". The material is soft, and soon erodes away when exposed to wind and weather. The spine of Mont Pelée was originally a most impressive affair more than a thousand feet in height.

The disaster at Tangiwai caused a great deal of interest in another method by which volcanoes spread destruction. This is called a "lahar", or volcanic mudflow. Most volcanoes have a considerable depression in the centre of the crater, and, between eruptions, drainage from the crater slopes fills it with water and forms a lake. If, either as a result of a renewed eruption or a lack of strength in the side wall of the crater, which is generally mainly ash, a breach can be started, the water flows down the mountainside, sweeping with it a turbulent mass of mud, ash, and boulders as it runs down the outer slope. The lahar responsible for the destruction of the railway bridge over the Whangaehu at Tangiwai was the result of a sudden collapse of the crater wall of Ruapehu, releasing the waters of the large crater lake in a very short space of time, probably less than an hour. All through the Tongariro National Park, it is possible to see rocky mounds which have been deposited by past lahars.

What relationship have these volcanoes with earthquakes? Naturally, when a volcano erupts explosively, the explosion gives rise to waves through the earth which can be recorded on a seismograph, and sometimes felt. The instrument at the Chateau Tongariro has recorded a great number of movements of this kind during the eruptions of Ngauruhoe, but far more energy than that communicated to the ground goes into the atmosphere as sound. The explosions from Ngauruhoe have been heard in Taranaki, on the slopes of Mount Egmont, and on the coast of Hawkes Bay. Big noises are not always heard at shorter distances, since the sound travels more efficiently in the very high atmosphere. During the last eruptions of Ruapehu, explosions connected with the mountain were heard at Upper Hutt, not far from Wellington.

Most of the explosions take place either in the crater, or in the vent of the volcano. Sometimes, however, there are underground explosions or movements of magma which can truly be called "volcanic earthquakes". Compared with the tectonic earthquakes to which most of this book is devoted, they are generally very minor affairs.

Volcanic earthquakes and crater explosions are most frequent when the volcano is visibly active. When the activity is on the increase nearby seismographs show a kind of movement known as "volcanic tremor". This takes the form of very rapid vibrations, generally less than a quarter of a second in period. When tremor first appears, it lasts only for an hour or two at a time, but as the activity of the mountain increases, it becomes more violent, and increases in amplitude. When the eruption is at its height, it is much less regular in appearance, not so much because the period changes, but because the vibration keeps changing phase; that is to say, it breaks off in the middle of a movement, and begins all over again. Hawaiian volcanologists have suggested that the tremor may be caused by molten lava rushing past the edges of projecting underground strata, making them vibrate like the reeds of a mouth organ. There are arguments against this theory, but no really good alternative has been put forward. Figure 51 shows tremor recorded at National Park.

Differences in the kind of material ejected by volcanoes are a clue to differences in the composition of the lower part of the crust. Volcanoes confirm the belief that there is a difference between the structure of the continents and that beneath the Pacific Ocean. In New Zealand, and in South America, the volcanoes are of the type called "andesitic". Andesite is a more acid rock than basalt, the heavy basic rock which is responsible for the dome-shaped volcanoes of the Pacific Islands. It is possible to draw a line around the circumference of the Pacific, so that all the andesitic rocks we can find lie outside it. This line seems to parallel the change from a continental to an oceanic crust, and roughly to mark out the active earthquake

FIG. 51.  VOLCANIC TREMOR
Due to an impending eruption of Ngauruhoe, recorded on the seismograph at the
Chateau Tongariro.

belt. There is, then, a close connection between earthquakes and volcanoes, but it is not one of cause and effect.

I shall say nothing here of hot springs, geysers, and boiling mud pools, for they are, of course, secondary effects, and the reader who would like to know more can find them explained in books on geology.

# CHAPTER TEN

# Earth Waves and Sea Waves

They take the rustic murmur of their bourg
For the great wave that echoes round the world.
TENNYSON: *Idylls of the King*

THERE is a limit to the useful magnification of a seismograph. The earth is never completely still. If our instrument is sensitive enough, we will record small continuous movements even when there is no earthquake. They are called microseisms. If the magnification is great enough to show the microseisms, there is no advantage in increasing it any further, as the only effect will be to confuse the record. Microseisms are very regular in period, generally in the range from four to six seconds, although there are others of shorter period which can be quite troublesome to some seismographs. Their amplitude is not constant, but changes from day to day. Occasionally violent "microseism storms" occur (Figure 52) when they become so large as to make the records unreadable.

Some microseisms, especially the short period ones, are probably due to human activity. If the recording station is near a town, the short period vibrations will largely disappear at night when heavy machinery in the factories is stopped, and the amount of traffic falls. We can get away from these disturbances to some extent by putting the recorders in suitable places, but there are still natural microseisms to be dealt with. It has long been known that they are less troublesome inland than near a coast, but the exact way in which the earth waves and the water waves are connected has only recently come to be understood.

Where there are long straight coasts or lines of cliffs, it has been suggested, the constant breaking of the surf could generate

125

waves in the ground, and be recorded as microseisms. There is no doubt that some microseisms do originate in this way, but when an attempt was made to track down the source of others, it was found to lie far out to sea. During the last war special networks of seismographs, known as "tripartite stations", were set up, in the hope that the microseism origins might have some relationship to weather disturbances. This proved to be

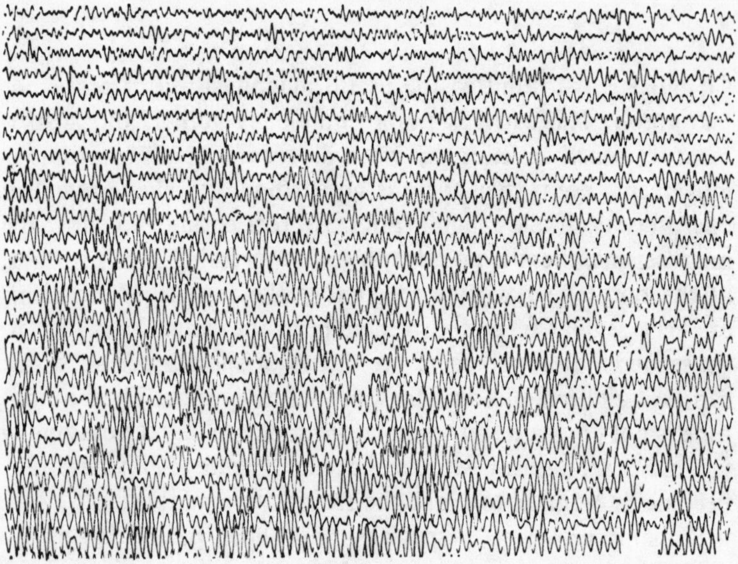

FIG. 52. MICROSEISMS

Section of a record made at Christchurch, showing the onset of a microseism storm.

the case. Intense meteorological systems, such as tropical cyclones, are the centres from which they spread, and it became possible to locate and follow the movement of storms by using the seismograph records. After further study, it was found that the ocean waves set up by the storm exert a kind of "pumping" effect on the sea bottom, and communicate the energy to the earth. These trains of waves, once started, will travel for thousands of miles, but suitable equipment enables the various separate sources in existence at the same time to be distinguished in many cases. So far there are only a few places where microseism observations are a regular part of the weather forecasting system. One of the most important networks serves the islands of the Carribean Sea. The use of the method is becoming more general, and at least one manufacturer is producing special seismographs for the purpose. The method would probably be valuable in providing hurricane warnings for our own Island Territories.

In addition to these storm microseisms, which have periods in the range from four to six seconds, and the artificial machinery and traffic vibrations of a second period or less, there are other short-period movements which result from quite local meteorological conditions. Chief among these are rain microseisms and frost microseisms, whose names are sufficiently self-explanatory.

Microseisms are for the most part a mixture of the different types of surface wave, and although their main origin appears to be linked with storms over the ocean and a few great lakes, there is only a small decrease in their amplitude as we travel inland. They can still be recorded in such places as the centre of the North American continent, and at the Soviet stations in Central Asia. It is quite possible that the presence of the low-velocity channel in the crust may play some part in the fact that they can be efficiently transmitted over such vast distances.

The story of microseisms is another example of something which at first seemed only a nuisance turning out to have a practical value. Perhaps, following the heading of an earlier chapter, I should have called this one "The Second By-Product".

There is another way in which earth waves and sea waves are linked, but this time the phenomenon is less helpful. This is the *tsunami*. Tsunami is the Japanese word for a seismic sea-wave, and is both a shorter and a more convenient term. These waves are sometimes referred to as "tidal waves", but they have nothing to do with tides, and as there *is* such a thing as a tidal wave, we should not run the risk of confusing it with a tsunami. Large earthquakes in some parts of the world are frequently followed by tsunami; and they often travel over great distances, causing damage in places which knew nothing of the earthquake. The Hawaiian Islands have often suffered in this way in the past.

Tsunami often follow the occurrence of a shallow earthquake beneath the sea, but Professor Gutenberg has established a number of cases where the epicentre of the shock was definitely some distance inland. It must therefore be supposed that they can be started either by changes on the sea bottom, such as faulting or slumping, or by some effect of the seismic surface waves passing across the shallow continental shelf.

Some of the stories told about tsunami are so alarming that it is not easy to separate fact from fiction. When they travel in deep water, the waves are extremely wide from crest to crest, perhaps several miles, so that shipping in the area does not notice them, even if they are several feet in height. When they reach shallow water, or are confined in narrow bays and estuaries, the water piles up rapidly and causes a great deal of damage. Even a wave five or six feet in height can damage small vessels in shallow water by bumping them violently on the bottom, and can destroy coastal roads and embankments.

The largest wave on record struck Cape Lopatka, at the southern tip of Kamchatka, in 1737, breaking at a height of 210 ft. Few other tsunami can approach this, but even the smallest ones are destructive. In 1952, a magnitude $8\frac{1}{4}$ earthquake in the same area caused a tsunami reported to have seriously damaged the Russian naval base at Petropavlovsk. New Zealand has not been greatly troubled by them, but in 1947 the bridges over small streams in the Gisborne district were washed away, and a small seaside hotel was destroyed by the tsunami which followed an earthquake near East Cape. In 1868, waves from an earthquake in Chile reached New Zealand with sufficient force to attract general attention in ports on both coasts.

Plate XXI

SUPERFICIAL SLUMPING. This road, crossing flat alluvial ground, cracked badly as a result of the 1928 Murchison earthquake.

Plate XXII

SUPERFICIAL SLUMPING. A surface sealing of bitumen is not sufficient to hold together a road laid on a poor foundation. This view shows the North Shore Causeway, Napier, after the earthquake of 3rd Feb, 1931. The swampy land on either side of the road was raised several feet, and is now dry.

Plate XXIII

**FAILURE OF BRICK-WORK.** This picture shows the typical X-shaped cracks which develop in brickwork. It is often assumed that the failure is due to poor mortar; but in this case, where the work on the building was still incomplete, the mortar has held in many cases where the brick itself has cracked across.

Plate XXIV

**TILED ROOFS.** The roof of Nelson Boys' College after the Murchison earthquake. Tiles have been damaged both by movement of the supporting framework, and by falling chimneys and architectural ornaments. Many of the upper rooms were filled with roof debris.

On the west coast of America, and in Hawaii, a warning system has been set up which should help to prevent loss of life. When the seismograph stations taking part in the scheme record an earthquake which could possibly generate a tsunami, they inform tide gauge stations, who watch for any abnormal movement of their gauges. If they find evidence of one, the places which the wave has not yet reached are informed by radio. The method can only be used when the tsunami originate well outside the area it is desired to warn. Those that affect Hawaii are usually from the Aleutians, and a warning is obtained from tide gauges along the Alaskan and Canadian coasts. The speed of a tsunami depends upon the depth of the water, and is about 400–500 miles an hour in the open ocean. It is only because the earthquake waves are so much more rapid that warning is possible. In the South Pacific, the seismograph stations do not have officers on continuous watch, and there are not many tide gauges. In any event, the places likely to be damaged are much closer to the possible epicentres, and the Hawaiian method cannot be used. The only satisfactory scheme for this part of the world is for any island which feels a strong earthquake, or sees an abnormal wave, to inform its neighbours by radio without delay.

Sometimes the sea gives warning of the approach of a tsunami by withdrawing before the wave arrives. When this happens, it is wise to make for high ground at once, but curiosity frequently gets the better of people and leads them to explore the area of sea bed which has been uncovered. This withdrawal does not always take place, and is certainly not a reliable enough effect to be used as the basis of a warning system.

Japanese observers have sometimes recorded flashes of light at sea before the arrival of a tsunami. There is no reason to doubt the reports, and it has been suggested that they might be caused by disturbance of the small marine organisms which make the wake of a ship so luminous in tropical waters. Whatever the truth of this, it still affords no basis for any kind of practical warning.

The frequency with which tsunami occur is hard to determine. The only lists which have been published are obviously very incomplete, and can often offer only a guess at the position of the epicentre responsible. Sizes are seldom given, and do not mean very much unless they are measured on an open coast or in deep water. Even small islands may sometimes cause a large "shadow" and protect the places on the far side quite effectively. It would seem that the Pacific has one or two a year, but that the majority of them are quite small.

# CHAPTER ELEVEN

# Safe as Houses

They dreamt not of a perishable home
Who thus could build.

WILLIAM WORDSWORTH: *Ecclesiastical Sonnets*

**B**Y now it should be clear that earthquakes are something we have to put up with, that there is little hope of prediction, and none of running away. The maximum violence in a destructive shock is generally reached within ten seconds of the first tremor, and all that can be done is to follow the advice of Dr. Bailey Willis: "Stand still and count to forty. At the end of that time, it makes no difference what you do." All this is not nearly so serious as it sounds. Most injuries and loss of life in earthquakes have been caused by the collapse of man-made structures. Sometimes they have collapsed because of lack of foresight; sometimes because the builders did not know enough about the forces their buildings would be called upon to withstand.

It would no doubt be possible to make all our buildings so strong that they would never shake down. This would undoubtedly be expensive, and probably inconvenient. Worse still, the buildings might be ugly; but the position is no different from one we meet quite satisfactorily at present—the danger from high winds. Occasionally a house blows down, or a roof blows off; but it doesn't happen often, and still less does it happen to all the houses in a large area. A reasonable standard of construction is enforced by law, and the whole community benefits. In the case of earthquakes, the position is not nearly so satisfactory. This is partly due to the reluctance of the authorities to lay down suitable building codes, and partly because the seismologist does not know enough about earthquakes and the way buildings behave during them to answer

131

quite reasonable questions. Engineers will be familiar with the view that a "factor of safety" is the same thing as a "factor of ignorance". For this reason, the science of engineering seismology has come into being. In New Zealand, its headquarters are at the Dominion Physical Laboratory.

If we look at the modified Mercalli scale of felt intensities, which will be found in the Appendix, we see that damage to buildings generally begins with comparatively superficial things, like cracked plaster, and extends through fallen chimneys to more serious matters like the breaking of foundations. Since most of us are more concerned about our own homes than about other buildings, we will consider how vulnerable the ordinary New Zealand home is to earthquake damage. It must not be forgotten, however, that the engineering seismologist is as much concerned with damage to engineering structures such as dams, bridges, and water towers as he is with private homes, office buildings, shops, and factories.

In New Zealand, as in most other countries, houses have certain national characteristics. Individual specimens differ widely from the type, but there is nevertheless a family resemblance. It is not my intention to comment upon their looks or their convenience, and these remarks must be regarded solely as a "seismologists'-eye-view". Our typical house is what the Englishman would call a wooden bungalow, and the American a single-storey frame house. The older ones have a "tin roof" of corrugated-iron sheet fixed to the rafters with lead-headed nails. In the newer ones, particularly in State Housing areas, tiled roofs are common. A few architects favour flat ones covered with fabric, tarred, and sanded.

From the point of view of safety in an earthquake, the tiled roof is a considerable step back from the tin one. Tiled roofs are heavy—many times the weight of the structure which has to support them—and some varieties absorb more than their own weight of water. This results in a top-heavy building, and the situation can only be partly relieved by additional cross-bracing of the framework. The warehouse at Port Ahuriri seen in

Plate XXVI is an interesting example of the behaviour of a top-heavy building with inadequate cross bracing. This was taken after the Hawkes Bay earthquake in 1931. Tiles are easily dislodged in a shake, and even if they do not cascade to the ground and strike the passers-by or the occupants of the building as they rush outside, they will probably be so badly cracked that they are no longer watertight. Plate XXIV shows the roofs of Nelson College after the Murchison earthquake, which were also damaged by falling chimneys and ornaments, many of which fell right through into the classrooms.

It is sound advice not to run outside in an earthquake, whatever the building you may be in at the time. The best thing to do, Dr. Willis's advice notwithstanding, is to get under some part of the structure which is reinforced, such as a doorway, or under a strong desk or table that will support the weight of anything that collapses on top. Falling material is responsible for most earthquake casualties, and as a rule more rubble falls into the streets than inside the buildings. In the Hastings Post Office, which is shown in Plate XXVII, the tower collapsed, killing a passer-by, but there were no casualties amongst the people inside.

Fortunately, there is seldom serious structural damage to the wooden house. The frame has considerable resilience, and can put up with a great deal of distortion before anything snaps. This flexibility does, however, contribute to the most common type of damage—a cracked pan in the water-closet. Since the cistern is fastened to the wall and the pan to the floor, a comparatively mild shake in the right direction will break it. Isolated instances are reported in shocks of strength between MM-4 and MM-5, but this is exceptional. Perhaps there is a case for flexible plumbing.

Damage to the water-closet is inconvenient, but hardly dangerous. This is not the case with the next most common form of damage—cracked and fallen chimneys (Plate XXV). These begin to fall about MM-5. Builders to whom I have spoken assure me that there is no reason why a properly erected chimney should ever fall, but they undoubtedly do. Some 20,000 chimneys in Wellington and the Hutt Valley were in need of attention after the Masterton earthquakes of 1942. The most common types of failure are a separation of the bricks, often along a diagonal, or in a kind of X-pattern, like the walls of the Napier Technical College (Plate XXIII), or a snapping off at roof level (Plate XXV). Individual bricks, or even the whole top section of the chimney can crash through a roof. There is little doubt that sentimental attachment to the open fire is responsible for the largest single earthquake hazard in the country.

It may be thought that the danger is limited to that of being hit by a falling brick. This is unfortunately not the case. Failure due to separation of the bricks is the greater hazard, but its operation is indirect. This occurrence of secondary damage is a commonplace to the insurance man. A small earthquake may, for example, break a pipe, and the escaping water damage large quantities of stored goods. In any large earthquake community services such as water, gas, and electricity are put out of action. Under these circumstances many a housewife is tempted to prepare a meal, or at least to boil tea on the open fireplace. If the chimney has a crack concealed behind the woodwork, the risk of fire is very great. Once a fire starts, the normal fire-fighting services are not available to put it out. This is not a far-fetched possibility. Records of the great San Francisco shock, and several more recent Japanese ones, show that the damage by fires lit after the earthquake was many times more costly than that caused by the shock itself.

One thing which is frequently overlooked when devising earthquake precaution schemes is the fact that not only will there be no mains water supplies available, but also it will not be possible to use wheeled vehicles until the streets have been cleared of debris, even if slump cracks have not made some of them permanently impassable. Many fire authorities are too ready to draw analogies with war-time air-raid experiences, rather than devoting themselves to the study of past earthquakes. In this connection, it should be remembered that photographers very often do not begin to record the event until after some preliminary clearing has taken place.

There are three possible ways of removing this hazard. The first is to enforce the building of chimneys in a single piece of adequately reinforced concrete. This would undoubtedly be expensive. The second would be to make every householder with a chimney install a tank, pond, or swimming pool containing enough water to fight possible fire. The third is to abandon sentimental attachment to traditional methods of heating, at any rate in closely built-up areas.

The failure of brick buildings is often attributed to the use of poor mortar, but a careful examination of Plate XXIII will show that in a number of cases the strength of the bricks themselves has been exceeded. It is most important that the corners of brick buildings, and those portions which may try to vibrate independently of the rest of the structure, should be well tied together. The failure of towers, like the one on the Hastings Post Office (Plate XXVII) is probably quite as much due to a difference in natural period from the rest of the building as to any inherent structural weaknesses.

Many of the older buildings in our cities were once ornamented with large overhanging cornices and battlements. Those which have not been brought down by previous earthquakes have now for the most part been removed by the owners, either in the name of "modernisation" or under the pressure of public opinion. There are still some places, however, where earthquakes are comparatively infrequent, that would be well advised to pay some attention to this matter.

The reinforced concrete or steel-framed building, which is typical of most of the larger constructions today, possesses both strength and flexibility; and although there may be superficial damage to partitions and curtain walls, they can be expected to remain substantially sound after even a large earthquake. In fairness to architects and builders, attention should be drawn to the fact that the great majority of well-designed modern buildings will survive all but the largest shocks, but much more

135

attention needs to be paid to the problems of secondary damage and fire.

There is more to making a building earthquake proof than constructing it of suitable materials and seeing that there are no loose bits to fall off. We saw in the chapter on seismographs how the way in which a pendulum would respond to a vibration depended upon the natural period of swing of the pendulum. The same kind of thing happens in the case of a building. All buildings have a certain natural period at which they tend to vibrate. If the earthquake waves have the same period, they will shake the building severely. If the period is very different, the effect will be much less severe. The engineering seismologist therefore begins by studying the periods of buildings, and those of earthquake waves.

It is possible to calculate the period a building will have when it is constructed. It depends on the way in which the weight is distributed, and upon the stiffness of the materials. These may be difficult to estimate, and the addition or removal of interior partitions or the storage of heavy goods may change the period considerably. Certain rules ean be laid down to help the structural engineer arrive at a good design. Once a building has been put up, the natural period can be measured quite easily, and it may be possible to change it if it appears advisable. The measurement is made by the rather obvious method of shaking the building, and recording its swings.

The instrument used for doing this consists of a set of rotating weights driven by a variable-speed motor. Plate XXXII is a photograph of the one used by the Dominion Physical Laboratory. The diagram in Figure 53 explains how it works. A and B are heavy weights rotating about an axle through O in opposite directions. In position 1 they are moving to the left, so that the axle experiences a force $F$ in the opposite direction. After a quarter of a revolution, the weights move in opposite directions, and their effect at O cancels out. After a second quarter turn, the force at O is towards the left. With this arrangement there is never any tendency for the machine to move up and down, but a considerable force first to the right and then to the left, is generated in each revolution. So that the instrument can be kept balanced, and will not have a tendency to twist, the weight A is split into two halves, and B revolves in between them. This is much less trying for the gearing and the bearings. There are various ways of connecting the vibrator to the building. The actual size of the weights used depends on how safe it is to shake the building, and how sensitive a recorder

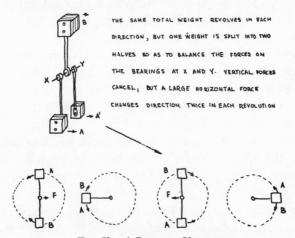

THE SAME TOTAL WEIGHT REVOLVES IN EACH DIRECTION, BUT ONE WEIGHT IS SPLIT INTO TWO HALVES SO AS TO BALANCE THE FORCES ON THE BEARINGS AT X AND Y. VERTICAL FORCES CANCEL, BUT A LARGE HORIZONTAL FORCE CHANGES DIRECTION TWICE IN EACH REVOLUTION

FIG. 53. A BUILDING VIBRATOR

The gearing to produce opposite rotation of the weights, the motor, and the frame for clamping to the building are not shown.

is available to measure the vibrations. In America, certain old buildings due for demolition have been turned into vibration laboratories and literally shaken to pieces!

Finding the periods of the earthquake waves has proved very difficult. Ordinary observatory seismographs are not a great deal of use, although they have given some valuable information in the past. The main disadvantage is that they are too sensitive and break down in a big shock. The other is that the speed of the recording paper is too small to open out the shape of the waves, and the shorter periods cannot be accurately determined. For engineering work, it is usual to employ special strong-motion seismographs. These seismographs do not operate continuously, and a special trigger starts the recording paper whenever there is a fairly strong earthquake. This means that the first second or so of the record is lost while the instrument gets up speed, but it has been found that this is seldom the really destructive part of the earthquake.

There are still only a few strong-motion records available in the whole world, and none of them has been obtained close to the epicentre of a major disaster. Since we do not know when and where a big earthquake will occur, it is difficult to lay a trap for it.

The ground on which a building stands has a considerable effect upon its behaviour during an earthquake. This can be studied by examining damaged cities, but only strong-motion records on a variety of foundations will really give the engineer the information he needs. It is certainly a sound practice to build on a rock foundation, and to avoid building different parts of the structure on different kinds of subsoil, such as partly on rock and partly on filling. One of the most unsatisfactory foundations appears to be alluvium—the material brought down by rivers, to build up the floors of their valleys. Japanese results indicate that a foundation of alluvium has the effect of absorbing small earthquakes, but it amplifies the vibrations of the larger ones. Unfortunately, old river terraces make apparently desirable building sites, and many small ports have grown up at the mouths of rivers. In such positions, very special attention must be paid to the foundations.

Most building codes today lay down some definite value of horizontal acceleration which a building must withstand. In New Zealand, the value varies from 0·08 to 0·16 times the acceleration due to gravity. In Japan, a more elaborate method is used. The country is divided into three regions, in which values of 0·2, 0·15, and 0·1$g$ respectively are taken as standard. These regional values are then multiplied by a factor varying from 0·5 to 1·5 which depends upon the building and upon the type of subsoil on which it is to stand. This type of code is gradually being replaced by a more elaborate consideration of the dynamic characteristics of the building, and use is now made of electrical models or "analogues" of the structure. The analogue is an electrical circuit in which the values of the components are arranged to give them a response to electrical vibrations that can be compared with the mechanical properties of the building. An ingenious photo-electric device then converts the record of an earthquake into a varying electric current which can be passed through the analogue, which is studied by the techniques of electrical engineering. The results can finally be reinterpreted in mechanical terms that will apply to the real building.

This is a most important field of seismology, and although our information is still scantier than it should be, some good results are being obtained by rule-of-thumb methods. More strong-motion records are badly needed, and the Department of Scientific and Industrial Research has scattered a number of them over the country. But many more are necessary, and this means spending more money.

CHAPTER TWELVE

# Some Famous Earthquakes

... The strong-based promontory
Have I made shake, and by the spurs pluck'd up
The pine and cedar:
SHAKESPEARE: *The Tempest*

EARTHQUAKES have always been the subject of rumour
and exaggeration. That ancient gossip writer, Pliny, tells
of twelve cities in Asia overthrown by earthquake; and Seneca
records the birth of two new islands, Theron and Therea. In
740 "The Citie of *Constantinople* was so wonderfully shaken
with an Earthquake an whole yeare together, that the Em-
perour thereof, and all his people, were constreyned to dwell
abroad in the fields vnder tents and pauilions, for feare that
their houses & buildings would fall on their heads".

Not all the ancient earthquakes were so violent. " 'Tis since
the earthquake now eleven year", says Juliet's nurse, and Shakespeare himself no doubt felt the earthquake of 1580. This shock
forms the subject of a pamphlet by Thomas Twyne, which contains more good sense and accurate observation than the
modern reader would expect from the title—"A fhorte and
pithie difcourfe concerning the engendring, tokens, and effects
of all Earthquakes in Generall: Particularly applyed and con-
ferred with that moft ftrange and terrible worke of the Lord
in shaking the Earth, not only within the Citie of London, but
alfo in moft partes of all Englande: VVhich hapned vpon
VVenfday in Eafter weeke laft paft, which was the fixt day of
April, almoft at fixe a clocke in the euening, in the yeare of our
Lord GOD. 1580." As far as the cause of the shock is concerned, Twyne hesitates between the traditional views of Aristotle; and a purely religious explanation of the shock as a

140

sign of God's wrath; but when it comes to describing what actually happened, he shows himself a keen observer and an accurate reporter. "Some imputed the ratling of wainescotes to Rattes and Weesels: the shaking of the beddes, tables and stooles, to Dogges: the quaking of their walles to their neyghbours rushing on the tother side . . . many not trusting to their oun iudgement, and partly also mooued with feare, ran out into the streetes to know if the like had hapned unto others . . . aswell elsewhere as in London, the very shakinge caused the Belles in some Steeples to knoll a stroake or twaine. The toppes of half a dozen chimnies in London .were cast down: many stone workes and buildings, for that they would not yeeld, are shrewdly shaken". A marginal note records "Two children sore hurt, whereof one died presently". This account is a pattern for many that followed it, both in the Old World and the New.

By far the most spectacular earthquake of earlier times was that of Lisbon, in 1755. This has some claim to be regarded as the greatest earthquake on record. If it is possible to believe reports, the felt area, which was certainly more than 700 miles in radius, extended from the Azores to Italy, and from England to North Africa. A source of confusion in the reports of this shock, which makes it difficult to judge the real extent of the felt area, was the widespread occurrence of seiches.

Seiches are wave movements in ponds and lakes, and they may be set up by the wind and other causes besides earthquakes. The water in a lake or an enclosed arm of the sea has a tendency to "slop" at one particular frequency, depending upon its size and depth. If this frequency coincides with that of the earthquake waves, it will resonate, and the waves will be magnified as if by a seismograph. Oscillations of this kind were observed in France, Italy, Holland, Switzerland, and England, and reports of the movements even came from Norway and Sweden, at a distance of nearly 1800 miles from the epicentre. In those countries, however, the shock was certainly not felt. In the great Assam earthquake of 1950, seiches were again observed at very great distances. There were oscillations recorded on the depth gauges at a number of English reservoirs, and also observations in Scandinavia. The very largest earthquakes seem to be particularly effective in generating seiches, possibly because the very long-period waves are still of appreciable amplitude at great distances.

In 1755, the damage to Lisbon itself was very great. At that time, the city had about 230,000 inhabitants, nearly 30,000 of whom were killed, according to conservative estimates. Great numbers of people were in the churches, for it was All Saints' Day, and the time of the first Mass. The shock was followed by a tsunami about twenty feet in height, and by fire.

The disaster shocked all Europe, and the moralists and the wiseacres were not slow to make capital of it. Voltaire, in a preface to his "Poem on the Disaster of Lisbon" rebukes people who contended that "The heirs of the dead would now come into their fortunes, masons would grow rich in rebuilding the city, beasts would grow fat on corpses buried in the ruins; such is the natural effect of natural causes"; but he secured the earthquake a more permanent place in literature by the references in *Candide*.

"The earthquake is nothing new," said Pangloss. "The town of Lima in America experienced the same shocks last year. The same causes produce the same effects. There is certainly a vein of sulphur running under the earth from Lima to Lisbon." Many of the learned men of the age would probably have agreed. The rest of the report is less factual, but draws attention to the fact that in former times, natural disasters of this kind were more the occasion for examination of the national conscience than for investigation and taking practical measures against a recurrence. "The University of Coimbra had pronounced that the sight of a few people ceremonially burned alive before a slow fire was an infallible prescription for preventing earthquakes; so that when the earthquake had subsided after destroying three-quarters of Lisbon, the authorities of that country could find no better way of avoiding total ruin than by giving the citizens a magnificent auto-da-fé." This was no doubt as efficacious as the products of Joseph Addison's "impudent mountebank, who sold pills which (as he told the country people) were very good against an earthquake". It may be noted that the University of Coimbra is now equipped with seismographs.

It is not possible to give an account of every major earthquake from those times to the present, but a list of the more important ones is given in the Appendix. Europe has fortunately been free from further disasters on the scale of the Lisbon earthquake, whether in consequence of the auto-da-fé or not I venture no opinion. Other parts of the world have not fared so well. The New World was by no means earthquake free, and in the New England colonies, the settlers speculated on whether the "electrical substance" drawn from the air by Mr. Franklin's new lightning-rods might not be responsible.

The age of scientific investigation was beginning, and after the Italian earthquakes of 1857, the Irish engineer, Robert Mallet, was able to visit the locality. In 1862 he published *The Great Neapolitan Earthquake of 1857; the first Principles of Observational Seismology*. These two volumes are finely illustrated with coloured lithographs, and are a seismological classic. Damaged towns and villages are described in detail. The direction of overthrow of buildings and monuments, the nature of the forces needed to produce the damage, and the patterns of isoseismals are all carefully discussed, and an attempt is made to frame general principles. Mallet was not content just to describe damage. He was also an experimenter. He investigated the speed at which earthquake waves could travel by using charges of gunpowder to generate a shock, observing their arrival by watching the surface of a shallow bowl of mercury. He was also responsible for coining many of our technical words, among them seismology, isoseismal, and seismic focus. The earthquake was not a big one, unless we measure its importance by the contribution to knowledge which resulted from it.

Seismologists are likely to apply this criterion to the San Francisco earthquake of 1906—a major shock by any reckoning. It was this earthquake which led Reid to propose the elastic rebound theory. The reader may feel that this is of less note than the destruction of 28,000 houses valued at about £22,000,000. Water mains were disrupted, and the inevitable fire followed. It was confined to an area of about four square miles only by the decision to dynamite rows of buildings which were still standing. The greatest damage was in the business area of the city, built mainly on land reclaimed from the bay. The San Andreas fault, the movement of which was responsible for the shock, is probably the largest and best-known of all active faults. It can be traced for some 600 miles from Cape Mendocino to the Colorado Desert. The area of damage in the 1906 shock followed the fault for about 350 miles of its length, but was only about 50 miles wide. The actual displacement of the fault was mainly horizontal, but the amount varied a great deal from place to place, the maximum being about 21 ft. Not more than 3 ft change in level was reported anywhere; and in places there seems to have been little or none.

Since the San Francisco shock, seismological progress has been continuous, and it is no longer possible to consider advances as the result of individual earthquakes. New Zealanders will, however, want to read something of the earth movements which have been a constant accompaniment to their history. The most important shocks are located in Figure 50, with their dates and approximate magnitudes, but before any of the shocks shown there, earthquakes in Fiordland were felt by the members of Captain Cook's expedition.

Wellington first began to lose chimneys in 1848, and on 17th October of that year, three lives were lost. This shock probably originated in the northern part of the South Island, and was responsible for the "Earthquake Rent" which can still be seen in the Awatere Valley. It is not much more than 18 in. in width, but it can be followed along the hillside for nearly 60 miles. Figure 54, which is taken from a contemporary New South

CHIMNEYS. New Zealand's greatest single earthquake hazard. This shows the very common fracture at roof level. The usual reinforcing rods prevent the top portion from falling, but do not prevent the crack and resultant fire danger.

INADEQUATE CROSS BRACING. A top-heavy warehouse at Port Ahuriri after the 1931 earthquake. Proper diagonal bracing of the lower floor would probably have prevented this.

Plate XXVII

DIFFERENCES IN NATURAL PERIOD. The difference in period between the tower of the Hastings Post Office and the rest of the building resulted in its collapse. Although a passer-by was killed, the occupants escaped uninjured.                 *Copyright, 1940, Time Inc.*

Plate XXVIII

CURTAIN WALLS. The brick walls of the Taradale Hotel collapsed outwards, leaving the remains of the structure supported on the 4″ x 2″ framed timber partitions.

Plate XXIX

FIRES FOLLOW EARTHQUAKES. Fire soon gained a hold on the business centre of Napier. Almost all great earthquakes have been followed by fire.

Plate XXX

STREETS BLOCKED BY RUBBLE. Most buildings collapse outwards, and before wheeled vehicles can be used as ambulances or for fire fighting, considerable clearing is necessary. This is Hastings, N.Z., in 1931.

Plate XXXI

HAWKES BAY EARTHQUAKE, 1931. A view of Port Ahuriri. Fire has a firm hold. Note that the slumping of the quayside is responsible for most of the damage to the wooden-framed buildings.

Plate XXXII

A BUILDING VIBRATOR. This is the instrument used by the Engineering Seismology section of the N.Z. Dominion Physical Laboratory. The protective cover has been taken off, and some of the alternative sets of weights are standing on the framework. The operation of the machine is explained in Fig. 53.

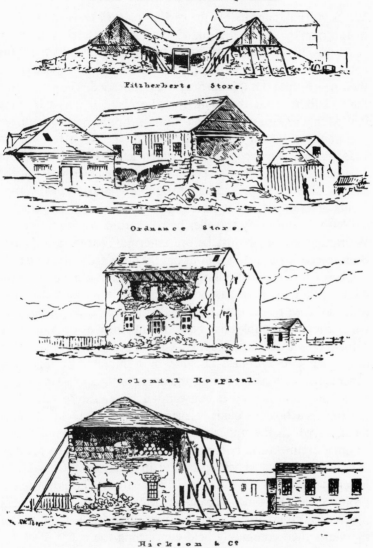

Fitzherberts Store.

Ordnance Store.

Colonial Hospital.

Hickson & Cᵒ

FIG. 54.  MARLBOROUGH EARTHQUAKE, 1848

These sketches of damaged buildings in Wellington are probably the earliest
pictorial record of earthquake effects in New Zealand.

145

Wales journal, is probably the earliest pictorial record of earth-quake damage in New Zealand. So large a shock within ten years of the founding of the city should have warned the colonists that special building precautions would be needed in their new home; but the warning went unheeded. They discussed the possibility that the thing was the result of gas becoming ignited in a cavern under Cook Strait, propped up the damaged buildings, and built many new ones in the same fashion. In 1855 there was a second shock which left Wellington without a sound brick building. The fault responsible was on the eastern side of the Rimutaka Mountains, and vertical move-ments of as much as 9 ft were measured in places. The trace is still visible, and every traveller by road from Wellington to the Wairarapa crosses it just before entering Featherston. It has been traced for a distance of about 90 miles from the coast.

Christchurch, like Wellington, has experienced large earth-quakes, though there has never been an important epicentre quite so close to the city. One of the more amusing aspects of Christchurch's troubles has been the difficulty of providing the cathedral with a fitting spire. The upper portion has been destroyed several times, in spite of a number of ingenious expedients, such as mounting the cross on top to swing like a pendulum, and having it consecrated by a bishop hauled to the top in a bosun's chair. Nevertheless, the present arrange-ment, in which the upper part is of wood, has maintained a suitable architectural composure for many years. The greatest of the Canterbury shocks occurred in 1901, near Cheviot, or Mackenzie as the township was then called. The government geologist of the time, Alexander McKay, published a very readable account of this shock. It begins with a summary of the views then commonly held concerning the cause of earth-quakes, reviews the earlier earthquake history of the district, describes the damage he observed, reports the opinions of the local farmers, and concludes with an anecdote about a horse which died of fright.

The main shock was on 16th November, and on the 20th,

McKay left Wellington for Christchurch, where he examined the cathedral spire, noticed that there had been a slight shift, and that "some repairs had been effected". The journey to Cheviot involved both rail and coach, as the train did not then run beyond Amberly; but he arrived at 4 p.m., just in time for an aftershock, which he did not feel. He remarks with some asperity upon the "eagerness of the press after the smallest item that deals with what is called 'stricken Cheviot'", for he seems to have been deeply impressed by a common aspect of moderate earthquake damage. It is not obvious except at close range. From less than a mile away "the township looked the very ideal of a country town, in nothing peculiar save that it was smokeless because there were no chimneys". When he entered the town, however, he found that the streets were littered with glass from broken windows, and most of the inhabitants, having pitched tents in the paddocks and harnessed the buggy for a quick retreat, had gathered at the post office to discuss the last aftershock. In spite of the fact that the town "when last visited was well provided with boarding houses and pseudo-hotels" (the last term seems to point to excessive geological thirst in a no-licence area) he had difficulty in getting lodging.

The damage he found was of the kind usual with wooden buildings. They had moved from their foundations, the chimneys had fallen—in many cases through the roof—and contents were badly disarranged. Superficial cracks and slumps appeared along the roads. On the following day, "a strong norwester continued to blow, which made it impossible to do any photography, and rendered work of any kind very unpleasant". For nearly a month he remained in the district, making general geological observations, and eventually returning to Wellington "direct from Kaikoura".

He records one of the earliest instances which has come to my notice of the direction of approach of an earthquake wave being determined by two people in telephone communication, one feeling the shock before the other. In this case it gave clear evidence that the shock originated to the north of Parnassus, a conclusion McKay had reached on other grounds. This was at variance with local opinion in Cheviot, which held that the shock had come from the east, or from the sea. These were honest opinions, but there were also some tall stories current. Mount Cookson, a limestone formation, was reported to be in eruption; and the bed of the Waiau River had been seen to open, first engulfing the water, and then as it closed again, forcing it to discharge in spouting columns which played to a height of 300 ft!

The other earthquakes I shall mention are probably within the memory of most of my readers, and many of the plates in this book have been taken at that time. The first is the Murchison earthquake of 1929. This had a magnitude of $7\frac{3}{4}$, and did considerable damage throughout the Nelson province. It was in a large measure responsible for the decision to set up a network of seismograph stations in New Zealand, for it was the first occasion on which there had been a large loss of life, seventeen people being killed. There was now a Department of Scientific and Industrial Research, and studies were made by officers of the Geological Survey and the Dominion (now the Seismological) Observatory. Even this disaster, however, was to hold its record only a few years. On 3rd February, 1931, the Hawkes Bay earthquake occurred in a more densely populated part of the country than any previous shock had done. The towns of Napier, Hastings, Gisborne, and Wairoa all lay within the destroyed area, and the death roll reached 256. The business areas of Napier and Hastings were almost totally destroyed, fires completing the work of the earthquake.

The Hawkes Bay earthquake was accompanied by considerable uplift of the region. Near Napier itself, the rise was above five feet, and large areas of new land appeared in the Ahuriri Lagoon. The total addition to New Zealand territory was about five square miles. About a fortnight after the main shock, a remarkable event occurred at Sponge Bay, near Gisborne. Men working on the beach saw a boulder bank rise from the sea, without previous warning, and without any tremors they could feel. The top of the bank is 7 ft above sea level, and covers about two acres.

There is now in New Zealand an insurance fund to compensate for damage from earthquake or war. This fund was established after the Masterton earthquakes of 1942, and is financed by a small surcharge on the premiums for other classes of insurance. From time to time the victims of floods and other natural calamities ask to be covered by the fund. So far, the Government has resisted the pressure, and it appears to have been a wise course to take. A single earthquake could easily involve the fund in payments of several million pounds, which it might still be unable to meet. Insurance is not a method by which payment for damage can be avoided; it merely spreads the payment in time and place. In an average year, some £1500 to £2000 is paid out for damage by minor shocks. Even a small increase in activity, like the magnitude 5 earthquake at Cheviot in 1951, sent the payments up tenfold. As far as this country is concerned, earthquakes are big business. In view of the sums involved, it might be worth while considering whether it would not pay the earthquake insurance fund to devote a small part of its resources to building research. Direct expenditure on seismology in New Zealand does not at present exceed some £6000 or £7000 a year; and the greater part of this is needed to maintain instrumental recording at its existing level.

# Facts and Figures

If a man will begin with certainties, he shall end in doubts;
but if he will be content to begin with doubts, he shall end
in certainties.

FRANCIS BACON: *The Advancement of Learning*

IN surveying the present state of knowledge about earthquakes, it has been impossible to do more than touch upon
the many branches of physical, geological, and geophysical
study which can be brought to bear on the problem. I have
said nothing of laboratory experiments upon the behaviour of
materials at high temperature and under high pressures; I have
only touched upon the ideas of continental drift and convection
currents. . . . But no science is learned from one book, or in a
few easy lessons. Few of us who claim to be seismologists are
able to discuss more than a handful of specialist problems with
any authority. This final section of the book brings together
some tables of figures and lists of historical events which the
reader may care to have for reference, and lists a few of the
books which may help the student who wishes to go further.
With this scant counsel, I take my leave.

## The Size of the Earth

| | | | |
|---|---|---|---|
| Polar diameter of the earth | . | 12,714 km | 7,900 miles |
| Equatorial diameter . | . . | 12,757 | 7,927 |
| Mean radius . | . . . | 6,371 | 3,955 |
| Radius of the core . | . . | 3,473 | 2,153 |
| Radius of the inner core . | . | 1,250 | 775 |
| Depth to the core . | . | 2,898 | 1,797 |
| Depth to the inner core . | . | 5,121 | 3,180 |
| Mass of the earth . | . | $5\cdot98 \times 10^{27}$ grammes | |
| | | =5,876 million million million tons | |
| Volume of the earth . | . | $1\cdot083 \times 10^{21}$ cubic metres | |
| | | =259,600 million cubic miles | |
| Mean density of the earth . | | $5\cdot517$ grammes per cubic centimetre | |

# The Geological Column

| Years ago | Era | Period | Duration (years) |
|---|---|---|---|
| | QUATERNARY | Recent | 25,000 |
| | | Pleistocene | |
| 1 million | | | |
| | TERTIARY or | Pliocene | 15 million |
| | CAINOZOIC | Miocene | 20 |
| | | Oligocene | 15 |
| | | Eocene | 20 |
| 65 million | | | |
| | SECONDARY or | Cretaceous | 55 million |
| | MESOZOIC | Jurassic | 35 |
| | | Triassic | |
| 190 million | | | |
| | PRIMARY or | Permian | 30 million |
| | PALAEOZOIC | Carboniferous | 60 |
| | | Devonian | 40 |
| | | Silurian | 30 |
| | | Ordovician | 50 |
| | | Cambrian | 100 |
| 500 million | | | |
| | PRE-CAMBRIAN or EOZOIC | Pre-Cambrian | |

## The Modified Mercalli Scale of Felt Intensity

I. Not felt except by a very few under especially favourable circumstances.

II. Felt only by a few persons at rest, especially on the upper floors of buildings. Delicately suspended objects may swing.

III. Felt quite noticeably indoors, especially on the upper floors of buildings, but many people do not recognise it as an earthquake. Standing motor-cars may rock slightly. Vibration like the passing of a truck. Duration estimated.

IV. During the day, felt indoors by many, outdoors by few. At night, some awakened. Dishes, windows, doors disturbed; walls make cracking sound. Sensation like heavy truck striking the building. Standing motor-cars rocked noticeably.

V. Felt by nearly everyone; many awakened. Some dishes,

windows, etc., broken; a few instances of cracked plaster; unstable objects overturned. Disturbance of poles, trees, and other tall objects sometimes noticed. Pendulum clocks may stop.

VI. Felt by all; many frightened and run outdoors. Some heavy furniture moved; a few instances of fallen plaster or damaged chimneys. Damage slight.

VII. Everybody runs outdoors. Damage negligible in buildings of good design and construction; slight to moderate in well-built ordinary structures; considerable in poorly built or badly designed structures; some chimneys broken. Noticed by persons driving motor-cars.

VIII. Damage slight in specially designed structures; considerable in ordinary substantial buildings with partial collapse; great in poorly built structures. Panel walls thrown out of frame structures. Fall of chimneys, factory stacks, columns, monuments, walls. Heavy furniture overturned. Sand and mud ejected in small amounts. Changes in well water. Disturbs persons driving motor-cars.

IX. Damage considerable in specially designed structures; well-designed frame structures thrown out of plumb; great in substantial buildings, with partial collapse. Buildings shifted off foundations. Ground cracked conspicuously. Underground pipes broken.

X. Some well-built wooden structures destroyed; most masonry and frame structures destroyed with foundations; ground badly cracked. Rails bent. Landslides considerable from river banks and slopes. Shifted sand and mud. Water splashed (slopped) over banks.

XI. Few if any (masonry) structures remain standing. Bridges destroyed. Broad fissures in ground. Underground pipelines completely out of service. Earth slumps and landslips in soft ground. Rails bent greatly.

XII. Damage total. Waves seen on ground surfaces. Lines of sight and level distorted. Objects thrown upwards into the air.

# Distances in Miles, Kilometres and Degrees

| 100 km= | 62 miles=0·9° | | 1°= | 69 miles= | 111 km |
|---|---|---|---|---|---|
| 200 | 124 | 1·8° | 2° | 138 | 222 |
| 300 | 186 | 2·7° | 3° | 207 | 333 |
| 400 | 248 | 3·6° | 4° | 276 | 444 |
| 500 | 310 | 4·6° | 5° | 345 | 555 |
| 600 | 372 | 5·5° | 6° | 414 | 667 |
| 700 | 434 | 6·4° | 7° | 483 | 778 |
| 800 | 496 | 7·3° | 8° | 552 | 889 |
| 900 | 558 | 8·2° | 9° | 621 | 1000 |
| 1000 | 621 | 9·1° | | | |

The seismologist's degrees correspond to degrees of latitude. The length of a degree of longitude decreases from the equator to the poles.

## A Reference List of Historical Earthquakes, 1500–1904

The following list covers the period in which reliable information is available down to the general availability of instrumental records. It has been drawn mainly from John Milne's *Catalogue of Destructive Earthquakes*. All European earthquakes of Milne's Class III (which destroy towns and devastate districts) are included. Outside Europe, I have listed a selection of Class III shocks likely to be mentioned by general writers. To these are added some less intense shocks of special seismological interest, or connected with other historical events.

Dates may differ by one day from those in other accounts, as it is not always certain whether writers are using local time or Greenwich time for their records. They have all been given in the present calendar, as the change from "Old Style" took place at different times in different countries.

The names printed in capitals are often used for convenience as "proper names" of the earthquakes to which they refer, but it is usual to state the year as well in order to avoid ambiguity.

| 1505 | July 6 | Persia, Afghanistan |
| 1509 | Feb. 25 | Calabria, Sicily |
| 1509 | Sept. 14 | Turkey |
| 1510 | Jan. 10 | Bavaria |
| 1511 | Mar. 26 | Adriatic |
| 1514 | Apr. 16 | Zante, Greece |

153

| 1531 | Jan. 26 | Spain, Portugal |
| 1549 | | Persia |
| 1556 | Jan. 24 | Austria, Bavaria |
| 1556 | Jan. 26 | Shenshu, China |
| 1590 | Sept. 15 | Central Europe |
| 1596 | | Nizhni Novgorod |
| 1609 | July 13 | Kansu, China |
| 1612 | Nov. 8 | Southern Europe |
| 1618 | Aug. 25 | Switzerland |
| 1622 | Oct. 25 | Kansu, China |
| 1638 | Mar. 27 | Italy, Greece |
| 1658 | Aug. 20 | Philippines |
| 1663 | Feb. 5 | St. Maurice, Canada |
| 1670 | Jan. 17 | Central Europe |
| 1679 | June 4 | Caucasia |
| 1687 | Oct. 20 | Lima, Peru |
| 1688 | Apr. 11 | Italy |
| 1688 | June 5 | Italy |
| 1688 | July 10 | Asia Minor |
| 1692 | June 7 | Jamaica |
| 1693 | June 11 | Malta |
| 1703 | Jan. 14 | Italy |
| 1706 | Apr. 10 | Iceland |
| 1710 | May–June | Algiers |
| 1718 | Dec. 10 | Cyprus |
| 1719 | May 25 | Turkey |
| 1721 | Apr. 26 | Persia |
| 1727 | Nov. 18 | Persia |
| 1728 | Nov. 28 | Philippines |
| 1730 | July 8 | Chile |
| 1737 | Oct. 11 | Calcutta |
| 1741 | Apr. 24 | Italy |
| 1751 | May 24 | Chile |
| 1755 | Nov. 1 | LISBON, Portugal |
| 1757 | July 9 | Azores |
| 1759 | Oct. 30 | Asia Minor |
| 1763 | July 29 | Hungary |
| 1766 | Oct. 21 | Venezuela |
| 1767 | July 11 | Zante, Greece |
| 1773 | June 3 | Guatemala |
| 1783 | Feb. 5 | Calabria, Italy |
| 1786 | Feb. 5 | Greece |
| 1786 | Mar. 9 | Southern Italy |
| 1789 | Sept. 30 | Perugia, Italy |
| 1790 | Apr. 6 | Transylvania |
| 1791 | Nov. 2 | Greece |
| 1796 | Feb. 26 | Asia Minor |

| | | |
|---|---|---|
| 1799 | July 28 | Italy |
| 1802 | Oct. 26 | Eastern Europe |
| 1805 | July 26 | Italy |
| 1810 | Feb. 16 | Candia, Greece |
| 1811 | Dec. 16 | NEW MADRID, U.S.A. |
| 1812 | Mar. 26 | Venezuela, Colombia |
| 1819 | June 16 | CUTCH, India |
| 1822 | Nov. 20 | VALPARAISO, Chile |
| 1823 | Mar 5 | Southern Italy, Sicily |
| 1823 | May 7 | Central America |
| 1825 | Jan. 19 | Greece |
| 1827 | Sept. | Lahore, India |
| 1828 | Mar. 7 | Siberia |
| 1829 | May 5 | Turkey |
| 1832 | Mar. 8 | Calabria, Italy |
| 1833 | Aug. 26 | North India, Tibet |
| 1835 | Feb. 20 | CONCEPCION, Chile |
| 1840 | July 2 | Armenia |
| 1846 | Aug. 14 | Central Italy |
| 1847 | July 31 | Nicaragua |
| 1847 | Oct. 8 | Chile |
| 1847 | Nov. 16 | Java, Sumatra |
| 1848 | Oct. 18 | AWATERE, New Zealand |
| 1853 | Apr. 21 | Sheraz, Persia |
| 1853 | Aug. 18 | Greece |
| 1855 | Jan. 23 | WELLINGTON, New Zealand |
| 1856 | Oct. 12 | Mediterranean |
| 1857 | Jan. 8 | Southern California |
| 1857 | Dec. 16 | The NEAPOLITAN, Italy |
| 1858 | Sept. 20 | Greece, Turkey |
| 1859 | Mar. 22 | Ecuador |
| 1860 | Dec. 3 | Central America |
| 1861 | Feb. 16 | S.W. Sumatra |
| 1864 | Jan. 12 | Chile |
| 1867 | Jan. 2 | Algiers |
| 1868 | Aug. 13 | CHILE-BOLIVIA |
| 1868 | Aug. 16 | Ecuador |
| 1870 | Oct. 5 | Mangone, Italy |
| 1872 | Mar. 20 | OWENS VALLEY, California, U.S.A. |
| 1875 | Mar. 28 | New Caledonia |
| 1875 | May 18 | Colombia, Venezuela |
| 1877 | May 9 | IQUIQUE, Chile |
| 1879 | Oct. 18 | S. Hungary, Roumania |
| 1880 | Feb. 22 | YOKOHAMA, Japan |
| 1880 | July 18 | Philippines |
| 1882 | Sept. 7 | Central America |
| 1883 | May 3 | Tabriz, Persia |

| 1883 | July 28 | Cassanicciola, Italy |
|------|---------|----------------------|
| 1883 | Aug. 27 | KRAKATOA (Eruption) |
| 1883 | Oct. 15 | Greece |
| 1885 | Mar. 27 | Greece |
| 1885 | Aug. 2 | Russian Turkestan |
| 1886 | June 9 | TARAWERA (Eruption) |
| 1886 | Aug. 27 | Greece |
| 1886 | Aug. 31 | CHARLESTON, S. Carolina, U.S.A. |
| 1889 | July 28 | Kumamoto, Japan |
| 1891 | Oct. 28 | MINO-OWARI, Japan |
| 1893 | Jan. 31 | Greece |
| 1893 | Apr. 17 | Greece |
| 1894 | July 10 | Turkey |
| 1895 | Jan. 7 | Khorasan, Persia |
| 1895 | May 13 | Greece, Turkey |
| 1896 | June 15 | SANRIKU, Japan |
| 1896 | Aug. 26 | Iceland |
| 1897 | June 12 | ASSAM, India |
| 1897 | Sept. 21 | Philippines |
| 1898 | July 2 | Hungary |
| 1899 | Jan. 22 | S.W. Greece |
| 1899 | Sept. 3 | YAKUTAT BAY, Alaska |
| 1899 | Sept. 30 | CERAM, E. Indies |
| 1900 | Mar. 22 | Japan |
| 1900 | Oct. 9 | Alaska |
| 1902 | Apr. 19 | Central America |
| 1902 | Aug. 21 | Philippines |

## Important Earthquakes since 1904

This list begins in 1904, because that is the first year for which instrumental magnitudes are available. It contains all shocks with a magnitude of 8 or more, together with the most important intermediate and deep shocks, which generally have a somewhat smaller magnitude than the shallow ones. In addition it contains shocks of less intensity that have been the subject of important researches, or have attracted unusual public attention. As in the list of earlier shocks "proper names" have been given in capitals. Magnitudes have been taken from the lists in Gutenberg and Richter's *Seismicity of the Earth*, from U.S.C.G.S. epicentre cards, from Pasadena station bulletins, and in a few cases from the bulletin of the New Zealand network.

| Date | | Epicentral Region | Magnitude | Focal Depth |
|------|------|------|------|------|
| 1904 | Jan. 20 | Panama | 7¾ | |
| | June 25 | Kamchatka | 8·0 | |
| | June 25 | Kamchatka | 8·1 | |
| | June 27 | Kamchatka | 7·9 | |
| | Aug. 27 | KOLYMA, Siberia | 7¾ | |
| | Dec. 20 | Costa Rica | 7¾ | |
| 1905 | Apr. 4 | KANGRA, India | 8 | |
| | July 9 | S.W. of Lake Baikal | 8¼ | |
| | July 23 | S.W. of Lake Baikal | 8¼ | |
| 1906 | Jan. 21 | HONSHU, Japan | 8·0 | 340 km |
| | Jan. 31 | Colombia, Ecuador | 8·6 | |
| | Apr. 18 | SAN FRANCISCO, California | 8¼ | |
| 1906 | Aug. 17 | Aleutians | 8·0 | |
| | Aug. 17 | Chile | 8·4 | |
| | Sept. 14 | New Guinea | 8·1 | |
| | Dec. 22 | SIKIANG, China | 7·9 | |
| 1907 | Apr. 15 | Mexico | 8·1 | |
| | Oct. 21 | KARATAG | 8·0 | |
| 1908 | Dec. 28 | MESSINA | 7½ | |
| 1910 | June 16 | Loyalty Islands | 8·1 | 100 km |
| 1911 | Jan. 3 | TIEN SHAN, Turkestan | 8·4 | |
| | Feb. 18 | FERGHANA, Pamirs | 7¾ | |
| | June 15 | Ryukyu, Japan | 8·2 | 160 km |
| 1912 | May 23 | Burma | 8·0 | |
| 1913 | Mar. 14 | Moluccas | 7·9 | |
| 1914 | May 26 | New Guinea | 7·9 | |
| | Nov. 24 | Marianas | 8·1 | 110 km |
| 1915 | May 1 | Kamchatka | 7·9 | |
| | Oct. 3 | NEVADA, U.S.A. | 7¾ | |
| 1916 | Jan. 13 | New Guinea | 7·8 | |
| 1917 | May 1 | Tonga | 8 | |
| | June 26 | S.W. of Hawaii | 8·3 | |
| 1918 | Aug. 15 | Caroline Is. | 8¼ | |
| | Sept. 7 | Kurile Is. | 8¼ | |
| 1919 | Apr. 30 | Tonga | 8·3 | |
| 1920 | June 5 | Formosa | 8 | |
| | Sept. 30 | Fiji | 8 | |
| | Dec. 16 | KANSU, China | 8½ | |
| 1922 | Nov. 11 | ATACAMA, Chile | 8·3 | |
| 1923 | Feb. 3 | Kamchatka | 8·3 | |
| | Sept. 1 | KWANTO, Japan | 8·2 | |
| 1924 | Apr. 24 | Philippines | 8·3 | |
| | June 26 | S.W. of Macquarie Is. | 7·8 | |
| 1925 | Mar. 1 | QUEBEC, Canada | 7·0 | 60 km |

| Date | Epicentral Region | Magnitude | Focal Depth |
|------|-------------------|-----------|-------------|
| 1925 June 28 | MONTANA, U.S.A. | $6\frac{3}{4}$ | |
| 1926 June 26 | Rhodes | 7·9 | 100 km |
| 1927 Mar. 7 | TANGO, Japan | 8·0 | |
| May 22 | KANSU, China | 8·0 | |
| 1928 Dec. 1 | Chile | 8·0 | |
| 1929 Mar. 7 | Aleutians | 8·1 | |
| 1930 Nov. 20 | IDU, Japan | 7·1 | |
| 1931 Feb. 2 | HAWKES BAY, New Zealand | $7\frac{3}{4}$ | |
| Aug. 10 | Atlai Mts. | 8·0 | |
| 1932 May 14 | Celebes | 8·0 | |
| May 26 | Tonga-Kermadec Trench | $7\frac{3}{4}$ | 600 km |
| June 3 | Mexico | 8·1 | |
| 1933 Mar. 2 | SANRIKU, Japan | 8·5 | |
| 1934 Jan. 15 | India | 8·3 | |
| June 29 | Celebes | 6·9 | 720 km |
| July 18 | Santa Cruz Is. | 8·2 | |
| 1935 May 30 | QUETTA, BALUCHISTAN | 7·5 | |
| 1937 Apr. 16 | Tonga | $7\frac{3}{4}$ | 400 km |
| 1938 Feb. 1 | Java | 8·2 | |
| Nov. 10 | BEHRING SEA | 8·3 | |
| 1939 Apr. 30 | Solomon Is. | 8·0 | |
| Dec. 21 | Celebes | 8·0 | 150 km |
| Dec. 26 | ANATOLIA | 8·0 | |
| 1940 May 24 | Peru | 8 | |
| 1941 June 26 | Burma | 8·1 | |
| 1941 June 27 | Central Australia | $6\frac{3}{4}$ | |
| Nov. 25 | West of Portugal | 8·3 | |
| 1942 May 14 | Ecuador | 7·9 | |
| Aug. 6 | Guatemala | 7·9 | |
| Aug. 24 | Brazil | 8·1 | |
| Nov. 10 | South of Africa | 7·9 | |
| 1943 Apr. 6 | Andes | 7·9 | |
| May 25 | Philippines | 7·9 | |
| June 30 | Celebes Sea | 6·8 | 700 km |
| Sept. 6 | Macquarie Is. | 7·8 | |
| 1944 Dec. 7 | South Australia | 8·0 | |
| 1945 Nov. 27 | Indian Ocean | $8\frac{1}{4}$ | |
| 1946 Aug. 4 | West Indies | 8·1 | |
| Dec. 20 | Japan | 8·2 | |
| 1947 Mar. 25 | POVERTY BAY, New Zealand | $5\frac{1}{2}$–6 | |
| 1948 Jan. 25 | Philippines | $8\frac{1}{4}$ | |
| 1949 July 10 | TADZHIKSTAN | 8 | |
| 1950 Feb. 28 | Hokkaido, Japan | $7\frac{3}{4}$ | 350 km |
| Aug. 15 | ASSAM | $8\frac{1}{2}$ | |
| Dec. 9 | Andes | $7\frac{3}{4}$–8 | 200 km |

(Murby, 1936) contains information about a selection of historic earthquakes, with isoseismal maps and similar material. *British Earthquakes* are separately covered in a book by the same author (Cambridge University Press, 1924).

Original scientific papers are published in a number of journals. The most important ones dealing mainly with seismology are the *Bulletin of the Seismological Society of America*, and the *Journal of the Earthquake Research Institute, Tokyo*. New Zealand authors usually publish their work in the *N.Z. Journal of Science and Technology*. Many seismological papers appear in the generalised geophysical journals, such as the *Geophysical Supplement* to the *Monthly Notices of the Royal Astronomical Society*, the *Transactions of the American Geophysical Union*, the *Annali di Geofisica*, *Annales de Géophysique*, and *Gerlands Beiträge zur Geophysik*. Russian work is appearing in the *Trudy Geofisicheskovo Instituta* published by the Academy of Sciences of the U.S.S.R. The Swiss *Révue pour l'Étude des Calamités* includes from time to time a valuable list of damaging earthquakes, and accounts of relief measures. A *Bibliography of Seismology* is issued periodically by the Canadian Dominion Observatory.

| Date | | Epicentral Region | Magnitude | Focal Depth |
|---|---|---|---|---|
| 1951 | Dec. 10 | Kermadecs | $7\frac{3}{4}$ | 300 km |
| | Dec. 8 | Indian Ocean | $7\frac{1}{4}$ | 100 km |
| 1952 | Mar. 4 | Hokkaido, Japan | $8\frac{1}{4}$ | |
| | Nov. 4 | Kamchatka | $8\frac{1}{4}$ | |
| 1953 | Nov. 25 | Honshu, Japan | $8\frac{1}{4}$ | |
| 1954 | Sept. 9 | Orléansville, N. Africa | $6\frac{3}{4}$–7 | |

## Major Earthquakes in New Zealand

The information in this table is a rearrangement of that given by R. C. Hayes to the Seventh Pacific Science Congress. The column headed $M$ gives the magnitude, $I_0$ is the maximum reported felt intensity on the modified Mercalli scale, and $r$ is the radius of the felt area, in miles.

| Date (NZ) | | Epicentral Region | $M$ | $I_0(MM)$ | $r$ (miles) |
|---|---|---|---|---|---|
| 1848 | Oct. 19 | N.E. Marlborough | $7$–$7\frac{1}{2}$ | 10 | 290 |
| 1855 | Jan. 23 | S.W. Wairarapa | $8\pm$ | $11+$ | 430 |
| 1888 | Sept. 1 | North Canterbury | 7 | $8\frac{1}{2}$ | 310 |
| 1893 | Feb. 12 | Nelson | $6\frac{1}{2}$–7 | $7\frac{1}{2}$ | 370 |
| 1897 | Dec. 8 | Wanganui Bight | 7 | $8\frac{1}{2}$ | 310 |
| 1901 | Nov. 16 | Cheviot | 7 | 9 | 280 |
| 1904 | Aug. 9 | Off Cape Turnagain | $7\frac{1}{2}$ | $9\pm$ | 410 |
| 1914 | Oct. 7 | E. Bay of Plenty | $7$–$7\frac{1}{2}$ | $9\pm$ | $390+$ |
| 1914 | Nov. 22 | N.E. North Island | $6\frac{1}{2}$–7 | $7\pm$ | 400 |
| 1921 | June 29 | Hawkes Bay | 7 | $7\frac{1}{2}$ | 500 |
| 1929 | Mar. 9 | Arthur's Pass | $7\frac{1}{2}$ | $9\pm$ | 430 |
| 1929 | June 17 | Buller | 7 | 11 | 470 |
| 1931 | Feb. 3 | Hawkes Bay | $7\frac{3}{4}\pm$ | 11 | 470 |
| 1932 | Sept. 16 | Wairoa | $7\frac{1}{4}$ | $8+$ | 200 |
| 1934 | Mar. 5 | Pahiatua | $7\frac{1}{2}$ | $8\frac{1}{2}$ | 370 |
| 1942 | June 24 | Wairarapa | $7\pm$ | 8 | 370 |

The largest New Zealand earthquake appears to have been the S.W. Wairarapa, or as it is usually called, the Wellington earthquake of 1855. The shocks with the greatest felt area do not appear in this list, as they have been deep-focus ones in the Kermadec Islands region. At least one of these shocks was felt as far south as Banks Peninsula.

## A Short Book List

There are very few books for the man in the street which deal only with seismology; and few of those which can be recommended without reservation. Of these only one is reasonably up to date, J. B. Macelwane's *When the Earth Quakes* (Bruce, 1947). Of the older books, *Earthquakes* by N. H. Heck (Princeton University Press, 1936) is probably the best.

This list is far from exhaustive, particularly when it comes to specialist works; but many of the books mentioned will be found to contain further references. Unfortunately many books, especially those printed in the United States of America, are very expensive; and it is a wise precaution to enquire prices before ordering.

Readers who want a good brief introduction to geology should have C. A. Cotton's *The Earth Beneath* (Whitcombe and Tombs, 1945) in their shelves. It is written by a distinguished New Zealand scholar, and draws many of its illustrations from that country. A readable and well-illustrated longer text is A. Holmes's *Principles of Physical Geology* (Nelson, 1945). Popular books on geophysics are rare; but Harold Jeffrey's *Earthquakes and Mountains* (Methuen, 2nd ed., revised, 1950) is a well-written book by England's foremost authority. If your French is adequate, do not overlook *La Constitution Physique de la Terre* by J. Coulomb (Albin Michel, 1952), which would be valuable in an English translation.

Those who would like to study a formal text-book will find L. D. Leet's *Practical Seismology and Seismic Prospecting* (Appleton-Century, 1938) outstanding for its comprehensiveness and clarity. Perry Byerly's *Seismology* requires more mathematical equipment from its reader, and only the mathematician will follow all of K. E. Bullen's *Introduction to Theoretical Seismology* (Cambridge University Press, 2nd ed. 1953); but many will find its valuable and extensive bibliography of interest. Dr. Bullen, now Professor of Applied Mathematics at Sydney University, is a New Zealander, and a world authority on the internal constitution of the earth. In collaboration with

Jeffreys, he was responsible for the calculation of the standard tables of travel times which are used in every observatory. He has also written a short monograph entitled *Seismology* (Methuen, 1954). This is extremely concentrated, and is intended for technical readers who have specialised in some other branch of physics.

By browsing amongst the more technical works the general reader will find much to interest him. *Seismicity of the Earth* by Gutenberg and Richter (Princeton University Press, 2nd ed. 1952) has detailed maps of the whole earth, showing epicentres classified according to the magnitude scale. An introduction summarises present knowledge on a variety of important seismological topics. Gutenberg has also edited *The Internal Constitution of the Earth* (Dover Publications, 2nd ed. 1951), a collection of authoritative essays by experts in many branches of geology and geophysics. Along with this should be mentioned Jeffreys's *The Earth* (Cambridge University Press, 3rd ed. 1952). This contains some heavy mathematics, no doubt in accordance with the belief the author has expressed elsewhere that "the easiest way to make a statement reasonably plausible is to prove it rigorously".

C. A. Cotton's *Volcanoes as Landscape Forms* (Whitcombe and Tombs, 1944) takes a much wider view of the subject than might be suggested by the title. It is written in a very readable style, and well illustrated. R. A. Daly's books *Our Mobile Earth*, *The Architecture of the Earth*, and *Strength and Structure of the Earth*, although technical, should not prove too difficult if given close attention. In still another category is J. R. Freeman's *Earthquake Damage and Earthquake Insurance* (McGraw-Hill, 1932), which contains hundreds of illustrations from all parts of the world, not only of buildings that were damaged by earthquakes, but of those that were not. This will interest anyone whose attitude to earthquakes is concerned with the social rather than their technical aspects. On the other hand L. D. Leet's *Earth Waves* (Harvard University Press, 1950) the engineer and technician. C. Davison's *Great Earthquakes*

# Index

163

| | Date | Epicentral Region | Magnitude | Focal Depth |
|---|---|---|---|---|
| 1951 | Dec. 10 | Kermadecs | $7\frac{3}{4}$ | 300 km |
| | Dec. 8 | Indian Ocean | $7\frac{3}{4}$ | 100 km |
| 1952 | Mar. 4 | Hokkaido, Japan | $8\frac{1}{4}$ | |
| | Nov. 4 | Kamchatka | $8\frac{1}{4}$ | |
| 1953 | Nov. 25 | Honshu, Japan | $8\frac{1}{4}$ | |
| 1954 | Sept. 9 | Orléansville, N. Africa | $6\frac{3}{4}$–7 | |

## Major Earthquakes in New Zealand

The information in this table is a rearrangement of that given by R. C. Hayes to the Seventh Pacific Science Congress. The column headed $M$ gives the magnitude, $I_0$ is the maximum reported felt intensity on the modified Mercalli scale, and $r$ is the radius of the felt area, in miles.

| Date (NZ) | | Epicentral Region | $M$ | $I_0(MM)$ | $r$ (miles) |
|---|---|---|---|---|---|
| 1848 | Oct. 19 | N.E. Marlborough | $7$–$7\frac{1}{2}$ | 10 | 290 |
| 1855 | Jan. 23 | S.W. Wairarapa | $8\pm$ | $11+$ | 430 |
| 1888 | Sept. 1 | North Canterbury | 7 | $8\frac{1}{2}$ | 310 |
| 1893 | Feb. 12 | Nelson | $6\frac{1}{2}$–7 | $7\frac{1}{2}$ | 370 |
| 1897 | Dec. 8 | Wanganui Bight | 7 | $8\frac{1}{2}$ | 310 |
| 1901 | Nov. 16 | Cheviot | 7 | 9 | 280 |
| 1904 | Aug. 9 | Off Cape Turnagain | $7\frac{1}{2}$ | $9\pm$ | 410 |
| 1914 | Oct. 7 | E. Bay of Plenty | $7$–$7\frac{1}{2}$ | $9\pm$ | $390+$ |
| 1914 | Nov. 22 | N.E. North Island | $6\frac{1}{2}$–7 | $7\pm$ | 400 |
| 1921 | June 29 | Hawkes Bay | 7 | $7\frac{1}{2}$ | 500 |
| 1929 | Mar. 9 | Arthur's Pass | $7\frac{1}{2}$ | $9\pm$ | 430 |
| 1929 | June 17 | Buller | 7 | 11 | 470 |
| 1931 | Feb. 3 | Hawkes Bay | $7\frac{3}{4}\pm$ | 11 | 470 |
| 1932 | Sept. 16 | Wairoa | $7\frac{1}{4}$ | $8+$ | 200 |
| 1934 | Mar. 5 | Pahiatua | $7\frac{1}{2}$ | $8\frac{1}{2}$ | 370 |
| 1942 | June 24 | Wairarapa | $7\pm$ | 8 | 370 |

The largest New Zealand earthquake appears to have been the S.W. Wairarapa, or as it is usually called, the Wellington earthquake of 1855. The shocks with the greatest felt area do not appear in this list, as they have been deep-focus ones in the Kermadec Islands region. At least one of these shocks was felt as far south as Banks Peninsula.

## A Short Book List

There are very few books for the man in the street which deal only with seismology; and few of those which can be recommended without reservation. Of these only one is reasonably up to date, J. B. Macelwane's *When the Earth Quakes* (Bruce, 1947). Of the older books, *Earthquakes* by N. H. Heck (Princeton University Press, 1936) is probably the best.

This list is far from exhaustive, particularly when it comes to specialist works; but many of the books mentioned will be found to contain further references. Unfortunately many books, especially those printed in the United States of America, are very expensive; and it is a wise precaution to enquire prices before ordering.

Readers who want a good brief introduction to geology should have C. A. Cotton's *The Earth Beneath* (Whitcombe and Tombs, 1945) in their shelves. It is written by a distinguished New Zealand scholar, and draws many of its illustrations from that country. A readable and well-illustrated longer text is A. Holmes's *Principles of Physical Geology* (Nelson, 1945). Popular books on geophysics are rare; but Harold Jeffrey's *Earthquakes and Mountains* (Methuen, 2nd ed., revised, 1950) is a well-written book by England's foremost authority. If your French is adequate, do not overlook *La Constitution Physique de la Terre* by J. Coulomb (Albin Michel, 1952), which would be valuable in an English translation.

Those who would like to study a formal text-book will find L. D. Leet's *Practical Seismology and Seismic Prospecting* (Appleton-Century, 1938) outstanding for its comprehensiveness and clarity. Perry Byerly's *Seismology* requires more mathematical equipment from its reader, and only the mathematician will follow all of K. E. Bullen's *Introduction to Theoretical Seismology* (Cambridge University Press, 2nd ed. 1953); but many will find its valuable and extensive bibliography of interest. Dr. Bullen, now Professor of Applied Mathematics at Sydney University, is a New Zealander, and a world authority on the internal constitution of the earth. In collaboration with

Jeffreys, he was responsible for the calculation of the standard tables of travel times which are used in every observatory. He has also written a short monograph entitled *Seismology* (Methuen, 1954). This is extremely concentrated, and is intended for technical readers who have specialised in some other branch of physics.

By browsing amongst the more technical works the general reader will find much to interest him. *Seismicity of the Earth* by Gutenberg and Richter (Princeton University Press, 2nd ed. 1952) has detailed maps of the whole earth, showing epicentres classified according to the magnitude scale. An introduction summarises present knowledge on a variety of important seismological topics. Gutenberg has also edited *The Internal Constitution of the Earth* (Dover Publications, 2nd ed. 1951), a collection of authoritative essays by experts in many branches of geology and geophysics. Along with this should be mentioned Jeffreys's *The Earth* (Cambridge University Press, 3rd ed. 1952). This contains some heavy mathematics, no doubt in accordance with the belief the author has expressed elsewhere that "the easiest way to make a statement reasonably plausible is to prove it rigorously".

C. A. Cotton's *Volcanoes as Landscape Forms* (Whitcombe and Tombs, 1944) takes a much wider view of the subject than might be suggested by the title. It is written in a very readable style, and well illustrated. R. A. Daly's books *Our Mobile Earth*, *The Architecture of the Earth*, and *Strength and Structure of the Earth*, although technical, should not prove too difficult if given close attention. In still another category is J. R. Freeman's *Earthquake Damage and Earthquake Insurance* (McGraw Hill, 1932), which contains hundreds of illustrations from all parts of the world, not only of buildings that were damaged by earthquakes, but of those that were not. This will interest anyone whose attitude to earthquakes is concerned with their social rather than their technical aspects. On the other hand, L. D. Leet's *Earth Waves* (Harvard University Press, 1950) is for the engineer and technician. C. Davison's *Great Earthquakes*

(Murby, 1936) contains information about a selection of historic earthquakes, with isoseismal maps and similar material. *British Earthquakes* are separately covered in a book by the same author (Cambridge University Press, 1924).

Original scientific papers are published in a number of journals. The most important ones dealing mainly with seismology are the *Bulletin of the Seismological Society of America*, and the *Journal of the Earthquake Research Institute, Tokyo*. New Zealand authors usually publish their work in the *N.Z. Journal of Science and Technology*. Many seismological papers appear in the generalised geophysical journals, such as the *Geophysical Supplement* to the *Monthly Notices of the Royal Astronomical Society*, the *Transactions of the American Geophysical Union*, the *Annali di Geofisica*, *Annales de Géophysique*, and *Gerlands Beiträge zur Geophysik*. Russian work is appearing in the *Trudy Geofisicheskovo Instituta* published by the Academy of Sciences of the U.S.S.R. The Swiss *Révue pour l'Étude des Calamités* includes from time to time a valuable list of damaging earthquakes, and accounts of relief measures. A *Bibliography of Seismology* is issued periodically by the Canadian Dominion Observatory.

# Index

163